HOW TO FIGURE THE ODDS

THE DREYFUS FAMILY MONEY MANAGEMENT SERVICE

HOW TO FIGURE THE ODDS ON EVERYTHING

by DARRELL HUFF
and the Editors of Dreyfus Publications

illustrated by
John Huehnergarth

DREYFUS PUBLICATIONS LTD.   NEW YORK

DARRELL HUFF became interested in probability and the odds while involved with statistics when he was working towards a Ph.D. in social psychology. He settled for a master's in journalism with Phi Beta Kappa from the University of Iowa. His books include *How to Take a Chance* and *How to Lie with Statistics*. (The latter has also been issued in a college text edition). He has written for many magazines, including *Harper's, Esquire, Reader's Digest, Saturday Evening Post, Popular Science,* and *Redbook.*

**DREYFUS
PUBLICATIONS
LTD.**

Jerome S. Hardy
PRESIDENT

Sally J. Reich
Martin Stone
VICE-PRESIDENTS

**THE DREYFUS
FAMILY MONEY
MANAGEMENT SERVICE**

Jay Gold, Editorial Director
Spero Yianilos, Sandylee Williams,
    Editorial Assistants

Heinz Eller, Publisher
John C. Tosarello, Marketing Manager
Rosalie Bruno, Business Manager

CONTENTS

A Note to the Reader 7

CHAPTER I
The Odds in Your Life 9

CHAPTER II
Sex and Probability 16

CHAPTER III
"The Law of Averages Says . . ." 25

CHAPTER IV
Taking Long Chances 40

CHAPTER V
The Odds in Sports Events 52

CHAPTER VI
Dice, Roulette, and Other Games 73

CHAPTER VII
The Odds in Bridge and Poker 94

CHAPTER VIII

   Gambling Systems   105

CHAPTER IX

   Genetics and Probability   116

CHAPTER X

   Statistics: The Odds on What to Believe   128

CHAPTER XI

   Insurance: Betting Your Life   140

CHAPTER XII

   The Rare and the Wonderful in Chance   157

CHAPTER XIII

   How to Think of Luck   173

APPENDIX

   Glossary   183

   Bibliography   188

INDEX   189

A NOTE TO THE READER

This book, like its companion volumes in this series, has been planned to be as functional as it is informative. For that reason, the typographic design for the text specifies exceptionally wide margins. These are meant to be used for anything that will be helpful to you: for notetaking, reminders to yourself or even doing arithmetical calculations. The editors hope you will find the margins useful.

The stock for these books was selected in part because it can be written on equally well with pencil, or ballpoint or felt-tipped pen.

The colored rules you will find scattered throughout the book are used to emphasize salient portions of the text.

— THE EDITORS

CHAPTER I

The Odds
in Your Life

This is a book about using an understanding of probability and the odds in your life. It covers a rather large number of remarkably diverse things because estimates of the odds are helpful in so many phases of life.

It is not a treatise on gambling, but it offers a long chapter on throwing dice and bucking roulette wheels and other gaming devices in such places as Reno and Las Vegas and Monte Carlo.

Why? Partly because that kind of information can save you from folly on visits to those places or similar ones. Gambling, modestly for fun or heavily in hope of gain, is one of the applications many of us occasionally make of the theories governing odds.

But gambling devices are also excellent models for understanding probability in other things. A flipped coin is a model for looking at equal chances—since there are just two possible outcomes of each flip, and heads is exactly as likely to come up as tails. A pair of dice is a model for more complex things, since each roll offers many possibilities.

It is because of this that almost any book you pick up on genetics or general biology or statistics will contain a section beginning "When you toss a coin . . . " or "When you roll a pair of dice. . . . " The function of such a section is to explain the basic laws of probability and the calculation of odds—because these tell us vital things about human heredity that are discussed in a chapter in this book.

For an informal look at the odds in life, consider the case of a man we can call Clarence Harper. A window washer by trade, he came to work one Wednesday morning and shortly thereafter found himself hanging by a single strap four stories above city concrete.

A safety hook had broken.

One chance in a thousand, he told himself.

This is a reasonable, if rough, estimate of the likelihood of an occurrence that is known to be rare but is by no means unheard of. Therefore, he went on to calculate, the chance of its happening twice in a day is no greater than one in a million.

So Clarence Harper went back to work. This time it was a fifth-floor safety hook that broke and left him dangling.

What went wrong with Clarence Harper's calculation of the odds? His logic slipped twice—just as his body did.

It is basic to probability theory that the chance that two independent events will both occur can be found by multiplying together the probability of each. So under this law, if one slip was a chance in a thousand, two slips are one in a thousand thousand, which is a million. Which is almost no chance at all. So far, so good.

If our window washer had been making his estimate on his way to work, he might have been justified in dismissing the odds favoring two falls in a day. But after the first slip the odds were changed.

The probability of one fall had become one in one —the mathematical way of expressing certainty, which describes anything known already to have happened. So the chance of that second slip had reverted to one in a thousand—not great but worth reckoning with.

Indeed, Clarence Harper might have refigured those odds entirely at this point. Assuming all the safety straps were of similar age, the failure of one could well suggest potential failure in others. One in a thousand becomes more like one in a hundred.

One good reason for calculating odds is to recognize when a testing program may be in order.

If you fail to examine the odds in your own life more closely than Mr. Harper did in this instance, you too may be left dangling.

Your dangling may be literal, from misreading the odds on safety of transportation or scaffolding or ice on a lake or even a chair used as a step stool. More likely it will be figurative. You can be left dangling if you under- or over-insure, choose the wrong gamble in a bridge or poker game or a Las Vegas casino, fall for phony statistics, unnecessarily risk producing a defective child.

You may mistakenly believe that dice can be "hot," that a doubling system can make gambling profitable, that a losing contest is worth entering, that there is such a thing as a "law of averages" that can help you win at roulette or coin-tossing.

Lightning striking twice

You may, like the window washer, risk your life on a supposition that some long chance—like lightning —won't strike twice. But in the real world the fact that a strap has broken, however improbably, has no influence whatever on any other strap. A place struck by lightning remains just as strikable as before— assuming it is still there.

There are two ways of looking at probability. One way deals with frequency of events, the other with our degree of certainty about them.

The probability that the next birth at your nearest hospital will be twins is around 1 in 100. This is based on frequency—about 1% of all births these days are twins.

What does the weatherman mean?

But what does the weatherman mean when he says there is a 40% chance of rain tomorrow? Forty out of what? Here he means that he thinks it may rain, but guesses the chances are slightly greater that it will not. (Or he may be hedging slightly, for psychological reasons gone into later in this book.)

But it is possible to convert one kind of probability into the other, by a slight stretch of logic. The forecaster may be thought of as saying that in his experience every 100 sets of conditions similar to those now existing have produced rain about 40 times.

There are a couple of laws of probability that will influence most of what is in this book. So it may be well to put them down now where they will be easy to find.

One has already been met: The probability of two independent events occurring is found by multiplying together their separate probabilities.

A second useful rule tells us how likely it is that either of two things will happen. Will you get either a queen or a king when you take the top card off a shuffled pack? There is 1 chance in 13 of getting a king and 1 in 13 of a queen, so the chance of one or the other is 2 in 13.

That's sometimes called the additive rule. The other, with equal logic, may be called the multiplicative.

Results of figuring probabilities are often expressed, as we have been doing it, as so many chances in so many. For the queen-or-king combination, it was 2 in 13. We could also give the chance as a fraction, 2/13. Or we could reduce 2 in 13 to 1 in 6½, or to 15+%.

When the chance of some event is 2 in 13, the odds can be given as 2 to 11 *in favor* of it. That is, out of every 13 draws 2 will be what we are after (those face cards) and 11 with be failures. If we prefer, we can turn things around and say that the odds are 11 to 2 *against* it.

All these figures mean exactly the same thing.

Learning about the odds got its formal beginning some 300 years ago, when a devoted gambler asked the French philosopher Blaise Pascal where his dice bets were going wrong. The science of probability and its utilitarian offspring, statistical method, were on their way.

Knowing the odds and how they work is still vital to gamblers—which all of us are whether we like it or not. We gamble when we make an investment or a speculation or a purchase. We play the odds when we choose a mode of travel, lead a heart at bridge or stand pat at poker, reach decisions about business, health, romance, family structure, our way of life.

How to become "lucky"

Who is a winner? Most often it is he who knows the odds. These arise out of established, but widely misinterpreted, laws of probability. Knowing what these are and how to apply them to life will lead you to more rational decisions. In short, it can lead you to become what is known as lucky.

CHAPTER II

Sex and Probability

Every engagement, every marriage, every child-birth, every divorce is a bucking of various kinds of odds well worth knowing about.

What will the sex of your next child—or grand-child or neighbor's child—be? This may not be quite an earth-shaking question, though sometimes it seems so. It is a matter deserving your attention, however, because it so neatly illustrates aspects of probability theory that you can use in figuring the odds in your life.

"How about it, doctor—will it be a boy or a girl?" Medical science being unable, short of extraordinary measures, to give a useful answer to this standard question, many a doctor has learned to turn it aside with a quip: "Well, it usually is."

Another approach welcomed by many a wily practitioner is to take refuge in predicting a girl if that is what the pregnant patient and her husband would rather not have. The theory here is that he will be correct about half the time (though actually not quite); and his misguess will be forgiven or forgotten in the rejoicing if the wanted boy is what turns up.

Neglecting a slight edge produced by the fact that a few more boys than girls (around 105 or 107 to 100, varying from time to time) are born, the sex of that next child is a 50–50 chance, isn't it? Or is it?

Some doubt about this has been aroused occasionally over the years by people like Mr. and Mrs. Grover Jones, of Peterson, West Virginia. The Joneses have 15 children, all boys. This achievement far exceeds the one in the popular song in which people who have had "nine sons in a row" are consoled with the suggestion that "baseball teams make money, you know."

There are two questions we need to answer about all this.

What is the pattern?

First, do children arrive in a chance pattern as to sex? That is, can we answer this boy-or-girl question precisely as if we were dealing with heads and tails in flipping coins?

Second, what does the chance pattern say about such things? And what does it warn us against?

When the Grover Joneses had 15 children,
all boys, were they beating the odds—or not?

So back to the Grover Joneses, working up to them
by way of some smaller families more like yours or
mine.

As a newly married couple planning to have only
two children, what are your prospects that the two
will be of different sexes, as you probably hope?

Well, what you get may be two boys or two girls, or
one of each. So a mixed pair is one of the three possibilities and the chance of achieving it is 1 in 3. Right?

No. What we've hit on is an ancient fallacy in figuring odds or probabilities. A few centuries ago it was
able to fool eminent mathematicians.

In fact, one of those three possibilities is actually two masquerading as one. What you may have, with equal odds in each case, is boy–boy, boy–girl, girl–boy, or girl–girl. Since two of these four pairs are a mixed batch, you have an even chance of producing just what you want.

But suppose that, in defiance of the zero-population-growth folks, you aim to have four children before you stop. Is there again an even chance that the sexes will be equally divided?

This more complex situation also can be looked at quite simply, if tediously, by listing all the possibilities. Girl–girl–girl–girl. Girl–girl–girl–boy. And so on. When you run through them all you will find 16 sequences, of which 6 will contain two boys and two girls. The chance that your brood of four will be evenly divided is only 6 in 16, or 3 in 8. The odds are 5 to 3 against you.

Two girls. What next?

Let us now turn to consider a brood already half-produced. Cal and Mary Andrus also had planned to have four children, preferably two boys and two girls. As of today they have two daughters. A third child is imminent.

How do their chances look now?

The sex of the children you may already have
has no influence on the sex of any to come.

"Hopeless," says Mary. "Girls run in my family for generations back. And we have just confirmed the tendency twice ourselves."

"I don't believe it for a minute," says Cal. "I say the chances are very much in our favor. We know that in general boys and girls tend to come in about equal numbers. Having produced two girls we can logically expect a couple of boys to balance things up. I'm as sure of that as I am that if a roulette wheel showed red several times in a row I'd be smart to back the black on the next turn."

What these parents have recited are a couple of common fallacies. Mary (who may not have stopped to think that she is descended from a precisely equal number of male and female forebears) is trying to establish a trend on the basis of an insignificant number of cases. Medical literature contains many examples of Mary's kind of statistical thinking. It commonly takes the form of boosting a new treatment after testing it on far too few cases.

Cal's notion has a long history, too. Known as the doctrine of the maturity of chances, it has produced a juicy lot of confusion in thinking about probability. And it has, in its time, ruined a host of gamblers, mostly amateur.

On the historic occasion in 1913 when black came up a record 26 times in succession on one of the wheels at Monte Carlo, disaster for the house might reasonably have been predicted. Except for the question of house limit, a player who had put one *louis* (about $4.00) on black when the run started and pyramided just long enough would have staggered out with $268,500,000.

But the maturity doctrine held sway among those present. The more times black came up the more eager the customers became to back red—which looked like virtually a sure thing to them. By the end of the phenomenal run this misguided behavior had enriched the casino by millions of francs.

Common sense somehow seems to favor the maturity doctrine: it just sounds reasonable. But common-sense reasoning easily shows its falsity. A tossed coin, a pair of dice, or a roulette wheel has no memory. The odds on any given toss, roll, or turn remain precisely the same regardless of the past.

Right for the wrong reason

This is equally true of human chromosomes and their genes. The chance that the upcoming young Andrus will be a boy remains the standard 1 in 2. The same goes for the prospective fourth child. Multiplied together (one–half times one–half is one–fourth) this gives 1 chance in 4 that both will be boys. With their two-girl start to handicap them, the Andruses can now figure the odds as 3 to 1 against a total brood that will be evenly balanced. In depressing Cal, this should at least cheer Mary because her prediction would thus be proved right—even if for the wrong reason.

We can investigate another aspect of probability by assuming, reasonably, that Cal and Mary will be at least a little pleased if they can break their possible all-girl string at least once. With two down and two to go, what is the probability that at least one of their children will be a boy?

Now it happens that these "at least" questions are, in all but the simplest cases, among the trickiest ones around. A good way to look at any of these "at least" problems is backwards.

Just as we found 1 chance in 4 that both future children will be boys, we could show that there is 1 in 4 that both will be girls. Unless this 1-in-4 chance occurs, at least one will be a boy. The Andruses can figure the odds as 3 to 1 in favor of breaking their string of girls. All is not lost.

Cases like that of the fifteen consecutive male Joneses have led geneticists to speculate, as one of them put it, that perhaps "some few individuals carry determiners which affect the X or Y sperms in fertilization." A writer on heredity has gone further and argued that the odds against such an occurrence "are so astronomically high that pure chance as a causative factor is virtually ruled out."

Let's see:

Obviously with a family of one child there are two possibilities and the chance that "all" will be boys is 1 in 2. As we have seen, with two children the chance that both will be boys is 1 in 4. With three it is 1 in 8, and with four it is 1 in 16, as already noted.

A pattern emerges

Can you see the pattern we're getting? With two children the chance that both will be boys is 1 in the square of 2—that is, two raised to the second power. For three children, it is 2 raised to the third power, which is 8.

The 1-in-16 probability we found for all boys in a family of four is discovered by raising 2 to the fourth power.

The chances: 1 in 16,000

Fifteen children, the number produced by Mr. and Mrs. Jones, might have been arranged in any of 2^{15} ways, or 32,768. Of all these combinations only two consist entirely of one sex. So fifteen consecutive sons or daughters is something to be expected about once in 16,000 families of fifteen kids.

It is a rarity, sure enough, but one to be anticipated now and then in any population in which many thousands of large families do exist. Chance alone not only *might* have produced this result—it could almost be *relied upon* to do so from time to time.

CHAPTER III

"The Law of Averages Says ..."

One of the most expensive sentences in the English language is the one that begins with the title of this chapter.

It has led to innumerable bad, costly decisions in every aspect of life from marriage to gambling to family financial management.

Long ago the American humorist Artemus Ward said: "It ain't so much the things we don't know that get us in trouble. It's the things we know that ain't so."

One of the things many people know that is not so—and often cite under the authority of that "law of averages"—is a doctrine properly described as the maturity of the chances.

You have taken a coin from your pocket and flipped it 5 times, getting heads every time. On the sixth flip, which are you more likely to get—heads or tails?

That's right. They are equally likely. And the very large number of people who believe that there is a law of averages saying it's now time for tails to turn up are dead wrong.

Why are they wrong?

In the long run, when tossing a coin you must expect an equal number of heads and tails—but there's never a "time" for either a head or a tail to show.

Because a coin has no memory. Each toss is completely independent of every other toss. Even after the unlikely—but distinctly possible —event of a hundred heads in a row, tails remains a fifty-fifty possibility with any fair coin, just as it was on the first toss.

Such a run of heads (or of red on a roulette wheel) should, however, arouse your suspicions that you are faced with a tailless coin or a badly unbalanced one (or a faulty wheel or a crooked one).

The law of large numbers

You will be much happier and probably richer if you think in terms of another law, the law of large numbers. It will not produce immutable truths or guaranteed winnings, but it will give you a far better picture of reality.

This one tells you that as you make a very large number of trials, the percentages of heads and tails will tend to be more and more close to even. But it also says—and this can be a little confusing—that the difference between the number of heads and the number of tails will tend to become greater with a larger number of flips.

Look at it this way. With 10 flips there is an excellent chance that at least 70% will be one thing— maybe heads, maybe tails. In fact, the odds against it are only about 2 to 1.

After 16 flips, the odds against a result this one-sided have jumped to more than 13 to 1.

But the probability that the number of heads will differ from the number of tails by 4 or more has become almost 1 to 1.

A million flips

These shift around for a reason not hard to understand: a difference in the number of heads and number of tails of, say, 5 is a large percentage of 10 tosses but a very tiny percentage of a million flips.

You may wonder how I know that the odds are about 13 to 1 against at least 70% of heads (or of tails) in 16 flips of an honest coin.

The answer to that is equally useful in predicting the odds for or against any particular distribution of sexes in a group of children.

It will tell you how likely it is that of 7 children born to a couple precisely 5 will be girls.

Or the odds against a flipped coin producing 5 heads in 7 tosses.

Or how much to bet against red coming up exactly 5 times in the next 7 plays on a roulette wheel.

The answer to all these questions is the same, of course. And there are a couple of handy ways of finding this answer and the answers to a lot of similar questions.

One way involves doing some algebra.

The algebra is at a level that wouldn't have bothered you for a moment when you were being exposed

to the subject in high school. In fact you covered it in some detail then, although perhaps not for the use we have in mind.

All the same, you can get the information without algebra if you insist. So if you are like my wife and find that the approach of an equation produces a sick sensation in the pit of your stomach you can safely skip over to that pyramid of numbers a few pages from here.

Nevertheless, I hope you'll stay with me if you know any algebra at all. Because the results are almost magical.

If you write $a + b$ and then write it again underneath and multiply you will get $a^2 + 2ab + b^2$. What you have done, you may recall, is squared the binomial or sum of two terms. You have found $(a + b)^2$.

If you have the ambition to keep writing $a + b$ under each product and then complete the multiplication you will discover that $(a + b)^3 = a^3 + 3a^2b + 3ab^2 + b^3$. And eventually, after a lot of tedious goings-on, that $(a + b)^{10}$ equals something that goes on quite a ways after starting out like this: $a^{10} + 10a^9b + 45a^8b^2 + 120a^7b^3 \ldots$

So what?

So—and this is the part that impresses me as a kind of magic—first observe the power to which you are expanding the binomial. In the first instance ($a^2 + 2ab + b^2$) we squared $a + b$, so the power was 2. Look at the coefficient—the numbers in front of the terms of the product—which are 1, 2, and 1. (Because in $a^2 + 2ab + b^2$ the coefficient of a^2 is 1, of ab is 2, and of b^2 is 1, even thought the 1s are not actually written.)

Who needs algebra?

Since what we have found is to the power of 2, these coefficients describe the possibilities in a family of two children. Of the four possibilities (found by adding $1 + 2 + 1 = 4$) there is one that both will be girls, there are two that the mix will be one girl and one boy, and one that both will be boys.

So the chance of a two-girl family is 1 in 4, of a mix is 2 in 4, and of both boys 1 in 4.

That's cute, perhaps, but not very exciting because we don't really need algebra to figure it out. For a large family, however, or for many tosses of a coin, we do need help. And that's where the binomial expansion shines.

Take a look at the product of raising the binomial to the tenth power, half a dozen paragraphs back, that began with a ^{10}. If you were to write out the whole thing and add up all the coefficients you would find the total to be 1,024.

Children, coins, red or black, odd or even

Since these are the coefficients from raising the binomial to the tenth power, we can use them to learn things about a family of 10 children. Or 10 flips of a coin. Or ten plays of red or black or odd or even on a roulette wheel. These varied events are mathematically equivalent.

So out of 1,024 possible arrangements in a family of 10 children, there is one that consists solely of girls. And, naturally, one that is all boys.

Looking at the second of the coefficients tells us that there are 10 possible combinations consisting of 9 girls and one boy. The third says 45 combinations consist of 8 girls and 2 boys. And 120 arrangements of 7 girls and 3 boys. Instead of carrying this any further, let's turn to an easier way of listing such possibilities and the odds of getting any one of them.

The self-calculating triangle

Three hundred and some years ago that remarkable Frenchman Blaise Pascal, whom we met earlier, found that if he started out to write all those coefficients we've been talking about in the shape of a triangle they virtually calculated themselves.

```
                1    1   (= 2)
              1   2    1   (= 4)
            1   3    3    1   (= 8)
          1   4    6    4    1   (= 16)
        1   5   10   10   5    1   (= 32)
      1   6   15   20   15   6    1   (= 64)
    1   7   21   35   35   21   7    1   (= 128)
  1   8   28   56   70   56   28   8    1   (= 256)
1   9   36   84  126  126  84   36   9    1   (= 512)
1  10   45  120  210  252  210  120  45   10   1   (= 1,024)
```

The top tier of this triangle, as you can see, consists of the coefficients of $a + b$, that is, 1 and 1. The second tier uses the coefficients of the binomial raised to the power of 2. And so on and on and on.

But the beauty of it is you don't have to do those calculations to obtain the numbers for the triangle.

Pascal made probability a lot easier to figure
by constructing the triangle reproduced on the opposite page.

By adding each pair of numbers in the second line
you find what to write just below the space between
them in the third line. Sums of the third-line pairs
give the fourth line. And so it goes.

You can see how it all works by adding another
line to the triangle yourself. First term, of course, is 1.
Write this just below and to the left of the 1 that starts
the last existing line.

Now add the first and second terms in that line
$(1 + 10 = 11)$ and write the result just below the
space between the 1 and the 10. Next add 10 and 45
and write 55 just below the space between 10 and 45.
Likewise your next term will be 165 and the one following that, 330. You can finish the line this way and
you can add as many more lines as you like by following the same procedure.

To make Pascal's triangle as handy as possible, I've
added up all the terms in each line and shown the
sum at the right.

Making the triangle work

Now you can find all the terms for the tenth power
of the binomial, a few of which we looked at earlier.
The bottom (tenth) line of the triangle informs you
that a family of ten children may be arranged in 1,024
ways. One of these is all girls (because the first term
in the line is 1) and one is all boys (last term).

So the chance of all girls in a family of ten is 1 in
1,024. The odds *against* this happening can then be
stated as 1023 to 1.

For nine girls and one boy, the chance is 10 in 1,024.
For eight girls and two boys, it's 45 in 1,024. (Since
there are also 45 chances in 1,024 of two girls and
eight boys, you can say that the chances are 90 in
1,024 of getting a 2:8 ratio.

The center term tells you that five boys and five
girls is the single most likely combination. It would
happen 252 times out of 1,024, which is almost one-
fourth of the time.

So it seems that for a family of ten, or ten flips of a coin, the odds are about 3 to 1 against a fifty–fifty result.

And also note that a 6:4 mix is *more* probable that 5:5. When you add the 210 chances in 1,024 of getting six girls and four boys to the 210 of getting four girls and six boys, you find 420 chances out of 1,024—which means the odds against this mix are not terribly far from 3 to 2.

We'll dig up some handy applications of this tendency in other situations, including how to lead at contract bridge.

But for now it will be most useful, having seen some ways in which the law of large numbers works, to cast a sharpened eye on how it doesn't.

An offspring of the law of large numbers

We are back to the false doctrine of the maturity of chances.

It is a natural child (which is an old way of saying bastard) of the law of large numbers.

One thing the law of large numbers tells us is that in the long run things like heads and tails tend to come up equally. The longer we continue that long run the more nearly certain we will become that heads will come up within any given percentage of equality you may care to choose.

For a mild instance of the form the doctrine takes, consider this passage from a new book by Ellen Williamson, *Spend Yourself Rich.*

"I have a system for roulette . . . sensible because it takes into account the law of averages. . . . Each time a new number came up we scratched it out on our little pad. . . . When there were twelve numbers left that hadn't come up, we began to play, covering each one with one chip. The theory behind this dazzling system is that, according to the law of averages, each number comes up every 38 times in the long run; therefore if twelve numbers or less have not turned up at all they certainly have just as good a chance to come up as the rest of the numbers, *and,* in fact, have maybe a tiny bit better chance than the rest as they are perhaps a bit overdue."

A brand-new condition every time

The trouble with the lady's system, as with all systems and with all ideas based on the mythical law of averages, is that a roulette wheel has no memory— as we've noted before in respect to coins and wheels and other things, and will have occasion to do so again.

Every single toss and every single turn is a brand-new condition. And each, or every, possibility is just exactly as likely as it was a minute or a week earlier.

Another aspect that adds to the confusion is that after a coin has, let's say, produced 8 heads in 10 flips the total expectation for the run has indeed been altered. If we've set out to make a total of 20 flips, the best guess as to the approximate number of heads is now 13 rather than the 10 that it was at the beginning. Because now we are estimating the odds for the 10 to come and adding that estimate of 5 to the eight heads we already know were produced in the first ten flips.

Anyway, the lady with the system goes on to confess: "I am sad to report, however, that I tried this good old system when I was recently at a casino just outside of Lisbon and I managed to lose about $100 with no trouble at all."

Something as regrettable as that could happen to you if you were to fall for a slightly more sophisticated version of the same doctrine. It comes from a book called *What Are the Odds?* by Leo Guild.

"Next time you have occasion to toss for something, remember this: if you are the one who calls, the chances are 3 to 2 against you. Seven out of 10 people will call heads. Heads, of course, will turn up only 5 out of 10 times, so if you let your opponent call you have far the better chance of winning."

Sounds vaguely convincing, doesn't it?

But it's easy to explode. From this example it would follow that if you called heads every time you'd do even worse. But, of course, if you do call heads on every toss you'll tend to be right half the time—precisely the expectation you would have if you always called tails, or alternated your calls, or simply mixed them up randomly.

How safe is a shell hole?

The illogical but persistent notion that what has gone before will affect what is to come, even in a pure-chance situation, takes another strange form.

In World War I it was commonly held among infantrymen that the safest place under shelling was a shell hole. The odds against two shells striking the same spot were astronomical, the veteran soldier would explain. True—for any given spot before it was struck the first time. Assuming the odds against hitting a given hundred square yards were 100 to 1, then the chance of its suffering twice would indeed be an encouraging 10,000 (100 × 100) to 1.

But once the spot was hit, the 100 to 1 chance had already occurred and now it offered precisely the same future odds as any other bit of the terrain.

CHAPTER IV

Taking Long Chances

The long-chance games are lotteries and numbers games and raffles, prize contests and drawings, bingo and football pools—and the prince of them all, the Irish Sweepstakes.

The long-chance games are the slow ones and the lonely ones. Instead of rapid action with a rather good chance of winning a relatively small sum, you are offered a single big gamble for a very large prize.

The odds are so enormously against you in some of these contests that you might play them assiduously all your life and never win once.

Or you might put up a nickel (actually tuppence) as an Irishman named Jimmy Gault did in 1959 and retire as he did with some $841,815. Tax-free too, if you lived in Britain and won it in a football pool.

How can you figure the odds on pools and raffles and lotteries and the like?

There are a couple of easy ways if you have a few facts to go on. With a football pool in which there are some 20 million entries each week, your chance of winning first prize on any given week must be 1 in 20 million.

Consider then the occurrence of some years ago when an Englishman won such a first prize—and ten weeks later did it again!

Read how an Englishman won against odds of 19,999,999 to 1—twice.

What are the odds against such a thing? About 40 trillion to one (it takes 13 zeros just to write the number), according to a report published about the event. This figure presumably was obtained by multiplying 20 million by itself, meanwhile inadvertently losing one zero.

Hmmm. Well now, how about that? Although rarer events than that occur (the specific hands that the four of you held on any deal the last time you played bridge, for example), such a rarity seems suspicious when it involves an interesting occurrence. We'll look into that distinction of "interesting" in a later chapter of this book.

For now let's just note that rarity can depend upon the point of view. As you start your season of entering pools you might well say that your chance of a double win was that tiny. But what about the question of whether there will be a double winner during the year?

A man who has already won once still has just as good a chance as anyone else—that is, one chance in a mere 20 million—in each succeeding week. The odds against him over the season are more nearly a couple of million to one.

That's still pretty long odds, of course. It's a little like the story of the lady who jumped to her feet at a geology lecture and excitedly asked the speaker to repeat his last remark. "I said the world might come to an end in a billion years," he told her. "Goodness," she gasped in relief. "I thought you said a *million* years."

Back to our calculations.

If you know how many entries there are in a pool or contest you know that you have one chance in that many of coming out with first prize. And if there are 100 prizes your chance of winning one of them is 1 in 1/100th of the number of entries.

Until recently that was not so at all in one form of lottery that went under the name of contest in the U.S. Some businesses, large magazines and oil companies among them, were conducting prize drawings that sounded most appealing. Listed prizes added up to hundreds of thousands of dollars. Even if you estimated that hundreds of thousands of people were entering, your chance of winning was probably worth at least a dollar and all you had to do to get your chance at a prize was drop your entry into the mail.

Big splash, little cost

But government investigation revealed that the drawing was made among all the numbers for which offers were mailed out, not from among those entered. Since most of the people solicited did not enter, most of the prizes were not won at all. The sponsoring company had found a way to make a big splash at little cost. Your winning expectation was literally not worth the stamp it cost you.

The rules have since been changed. All prizes must be awarded. So now you can figure the value of a lottery or contest by dividing the value of all the prizes by the number of entries. If this figure is more than you must pay to enter, your expectation is favorable.

The pleasure of a little gamble

It won't come out that way, of course, in any lottery or raffle intended to make money. When you enter something of this sort you must assume you will tend to pay more than you will get. This can be perfectly intelligent, of course, if you are taking out the difference in the pleasure of the little gamble or in the knowledge that the difference is going to a good cause.

The other kind of calculation you can make to ascertain odds depends upon known—or estimated—probability of some occurrence. The person or institution operating the lottery or pool backs this estimate, and you need not care how many people are entering.

In this situation you are backing your estimate of the odds against the official one. If you truly know more about the situation (the true ability of the horse or football team or the condition of the starting pitcher's arm) than the pool operator, the odds actually favor you.

In that case, you win. But does he lose? Not if he has succeeded in getting enough bets on the other

Knowing the condition of a horse,
a football team or a pitcher's arm can
make you a formidable bettor.

team, or horses, to balance yours. Or has been able
to place bets of his own with an even bigger operator.

If he hasn't done either of these things and the
public's estimate of the true odds is far better than
his, he must either pay off painfully—or disappear.
You must consider this final probability in figuring the
odds against winning and collecting.

The famous and still popular "numbers" game is a form of lottery in which the odds are absolutely known—though perhaps not to most of the people who contribute to the total of several billion dollars a year bet in this way. Even if you're not one of those contributors—found most frequently in Harlem or other city slums—you probably know how it works. A shifty little man collects 50 cents or a dollar from you, giving you the right to name any three-digit number you wish.

The number you are trying to guess may be the last three digits of the New York Clearing House report for a specified date. This, or any other widely published figure that cannot be predicted or rigged, will serve.

A thousand dollars in, $600 out

If you pay $1 for the privilege the payoff will be usually set at somewhere around $600. Since there are 1,000 ways to arrange the 10 digits, including zero—that is, all the numbers from 0 to 999—the true odds are 1 in 1,000. The numbers bosses will take in $1,000 for every $600 they pay out.

The $400 difference takes care of paying salesmen, overhead, bribes, profit.

The numbers people know that one set of digits is just as likely to come up as any other. In the long run their margin will be just what we have calculated.

But there is one danger. What if by chance a number comes up that happens to have been chosen by a large part of the customers for some reason? To keep their take as reliable as possible, the numbers operators often reduce the payoff (announcing this in advance, of course) for any number they feel might be played heavily. This list of "cut numbers," paying perhaps only 400 to 1, may include all triplets (000, 111, etc.), the current batting average of a popular ballplayer, and any "lucky" combination such as 711.

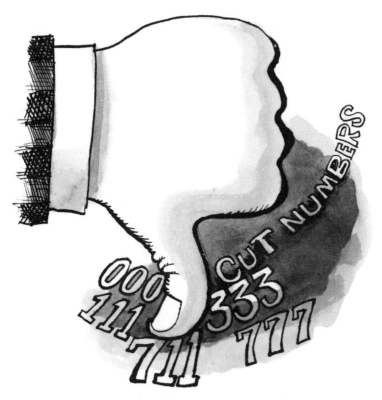

In the "numbers" or policy game,
the operators reduce the payoff on any
combination that might be bet heavily.

There are some other gimmicks in most numbers, or policy, games. But the important thing to know is that for every $100 you put up you can expect less than $60 back. Those special stipulations plus a 10% cut commonly taken from winnings by the "runner" who picks up your bet reduce your expectation even further.

If you start a week's play with $100 spread over as many numbers as possible, and put your winnings back in daily, you can expect to run that $100 down to about $3 in seven days.

Bingo is a lottery made to resemble a game. Since you help make the comparison between your number and the one drawn you have the illusion of being in a contest.

The "value" of a game of bingo in terms of how much you win multiplied by the chance of winning is found just as with any lottery. If it's an honest game and 100 people are playing you have 1 chance in 100 of winning. Divide the prize total by the number of players and your share is the value of the game to you. Whatever amount above this you pay for your card is the price of the entertainment you get.

What if you buy more than one card, as any real bingo nut will do? You double or triple or quadruple your chance of winning and the value of your expectation. You similarly increase your cost and your deficit—so you are paying more per hour for the entertainment.

One other thing you may wonder about if you have ever bingoed is the special large prize offered for covering your entire card—usually 24 squares plus a "free" one that is covered automatically—in some limited number of draws. John Scarne, who knows more about gambling than anybody, has invested many hours in figuring that if you succeed in doing it within a draw of 50 numbers you have bucked odds of 212,084 to 1. But it takes only 5 more draws to cut the odds to 10,304 to 1.

Lotteries in general offer you the worst gambling odds going. They commonly keep up to half or more of the money they take in, something no Nevada casino would even aspire to. (They'd hate it. They know such blatantly bad odds would discourage all but the stupidest gamblers and wreck business in a very short time.)

One of the best of the lotteries, it must be said—while recognizing that Americans who participate are breaking the law—is the Irish Sweepstakes.

In its favor must be said that it pays out more than one-third of what it takes in, with much of the rest going to the good cause of Irish hospitals.

As an investment, all the same, the Sweeps leave something to be desired. It is hard to avoid the counterfeit tickets that circulate constantly; inevitably they carry the same warning against counterfeits that the genuine tickets do. The instant you win your government loses interest in the fact that the whole thing is illegal and clamps a lien on you for the income tax due on your winnings. If yours is a large prize this will cut your net to far below half what you thought you were getting. (If you have a family who will share in the profits if you win, buy your ticket jointly with them. This can cut the tax to well below 50%. But you have to think of this when you buy, not when you win.)

You may wonder—as you read on and find I have no enthusiasm for casino gambles that take only a small percentage of your stake on each gamble—how can I tolerate for a moment a lottery take such as this one?

Mathematically almost any lottery is far worse than an average slot machine—and far, far greedier than a casino game.

But any bet at extremely long odds brings up a kind of psychological expectation. It opens a debate that has fascinated theoreticians for centuries.

It goes like this: Is a one-millionth chance of a million dollars worth the same as a dollar for sure or half a chance at $2?

By mathematical expectation they are all equal; each is worth $1.

This is a subjective question. The comparative value you would ascribe to each is perhaps not the same as it is for me; and certainly different from the conclusion that might be reached by Howard Hughes or any other billionaire.

You might enjoy comparing yourself with others in this respect. A group of middle-income Americans were once asked to choose between several pairs of alternatives of equal mathematical worth.

Most preferred 1/10 chance of $1 to a dime and 1/10 chance of $10 to a sure $1. When the latter offer was multiplied by 10 and then by 10 again, replies varied but most people who took the gamble for the $100 also took it for the $1,000. However, everyone preferred a sure million dollars to the 1/10 chance at ten million.

These results, reasonably enough, square with experience that most people are eager to gamble sums they can afford, only occasionally go for risks at levels that could hurt, and very rarely plunge heavily.

CHAPTER V

The Odds in Sports Events

Whether you bowl, golf, or knock around ping-pong or tennis balls, you can improve your win percentage by honing your strategy on the stone of probability.

If the bolder route to a tricky hole at golf will usually gain you a stroke if it succeeds and lose you two if it fails, it's a bad gamble if your mental record says you don't make it more than half the time.

For some deadpan thoughts on odds applied to golf, we could look at an essay by the late Canadian humorist (and economist) Stephen Leacock, who wondered if the time will ever come "when I shall make not one hole in bogey but all the holes?" Since bogey has come to mean a rather mediocre level—

one over par—you may prefer to read "par" for "bogey" in applying this logic to your own game. You'll also have to assume, as Leacock did, that you're playing a 9-hole course and—more dreadfully —that your game is never going to improve.

Merely time and patience

"The answer," Leacock concludes, "is overwhelmingly 'yes.' The thing is a mere matter of time and patience . . . a simple instance of what is called the mathematical theory of probability. If a player usually and generally makes one hole in bogey, or comes close to it, his chance of making any one particular hole in bogey is 1 in 9. Let us say, for easier calculation, that it is 1 in 10. When he makes it, his chance of doing the same on the next hole is also 1 in 10; therefore taken from the start, his chance of making the two holes successively in bogey is one tenth of a tenth chance. In other words, it is 1 in 100.

"The reader sees already how encouraging the calculation is. Here is at last something definite about his progress. Let us carry it farther. His chance of making three holes in bogey, one after the other, will be 1 in 1000, his chance of four, 1 in 10,000, and his chance of making the whole round in bogey will be exactly 1 in 1,000,000,000—that is, 1 in a billion games.

"In other words, all he has to do is to keep right on. But for how long? he asks. How long will it take, playing the ordinary number of games in a month, to play a billion? Will it take several years? Yes, it will.

What did he do? Played a billion games of
golf in 10 billion years to get the
score he yearned to get.

"An ordinary player plays about a hundred games
in a year and will, therefore, play a billion games in
exactly 10,000,000 years. That gives us precisely the
time it will need for persons like the reader and my-
self to go around in bogey."

Many sports offer situations comparable to those
found in tennis. For this sport Dr. Paul Heretelendy
came up with some calculations on the odds late
in 1971.

His most surprising—and inspiring, if tennis is your sport—conclusion is that in some kinds of matches you'll win 64% of the time if you can contrive to take a mere 51% of the points. And they don't even have to come at especially strategic times.

By computing the probabilities of all the possible point scores within one game, he has discovered that if you take 51% of the points, you will *in the long run* win 52.5% of the games . . . and 57.4% of the sets.

And that's if you play a two–sets–out–of–three match. Hold out for a three–out–of–five and the same tiny edge in total points should win you a nice 63.9% of the matches. That means you are winning 77% more matches than you are losing. Not bad for a 1% initial edge.

A much simpler calculation, and highly useful, is one I have made about serving in tennis. Again, it can have its use as a model for your own calculations about other sports.

One tennis rule that we have come to take for granted is actually rather peculiar. The player starting the point is given a special advantage: he is allowed two attempts at driving the ball into the service court, and the score is not affected by whether he uses both or only one.

As a tennis player you are likely to be told that you should get about 7 out of 10 of your first serves in. If you do much worse than that you are wasting that first serve, and if you do much better you are throwing away the privilege of a second serve.

A second serve, of course, is expected to be more conservative than a first one. I have come to the conclusion that it can be tested by the rule that it should go in 9 times out of 10.

Here's the math that says these two rules combine to give an optimum result. Such a result is one that does not include more double faults—missing on both attempts to serve—than you can afford, yet

doesn't ask you to baby your serves and risk having them (or, in doubles, your partner) murdered.

If you're getting 7 first serves in out of 10, you will have to deliver a second serve only 30% of the time. Miss one-tenth of these and you will double fault one-tenth of 30% of the time. That's 3 double faults out of 100 service points, or about one double fault for each player or team to the average set . . . usually an acceptable level, especially for a player who is pushing himself in an effort to improve his game.

It is worth repeating while we're about it the law that says when two events are independent of each other the chance that both will occur is found by multiplying their separate probabilities together.

Since we wanted to know the odds for a double fault, we multiplied together the chance of a bad first serve (30%) and of a bad second one (10%).

This illustrates another useful principle. When you have a question of "at least one" it helps, as we saw earlier, to approach the problem backwards. That is, consider not the chance of success on each move but the chance of failure.

Serving in tennis is an "at least one" problem because it makes no difference so far as scoring is concerned whether it is the first or the second serve that is good.

We'll find many opportunities to use this essential technique on a variety of subjects in other chapters. For now let's apply it just once more.

A champion pitcher of horseshoes

You're a horseshoe pitcher of championship caliber, let's say, and your record for the season shows you are pitching about 50% ringers. With the next 4 shoes you must pitch at least 1 ringer to set a record of some kind or other.

How likely is it that you will succeed? To put it another way, what odds should a supporter of yours offer in placing a bet on you now?

At first blush it may appear that this is a simple problem. Since you get ringers half the time, the average expectation in 4 pitches is 2 ringers, isn't it? True. But that's no guarantee. We all know that even a 50-percenter *can* miss 4 times running.

So try the backwards approach. To fail this test you must miss 4 times. The chance of missing on each toss is one-half. One-half times one-half times one-half times one-half (4 tosses) is one-sixteenth. This says that out of every 16 4-toss sequences you can expect to fail once and succeed 15 times. The odds are 15 to 1, and your backer should be prepared to wager $15 against $1.

Against an unsophisticated bettor he can probably get more favorable odds than that, however;
and that's why people who know the odds are the
long-run winners.

Baseball betting with a bookmaker is a simple
affair, especially from the bookie's point of view.

Consider a game between teams that are evenly
matched. The bookie quotes 6 to 5 either way. You
pick the team and put up $6 against the bookie's $5.

For each pair of such bets, one on the Giants,
say, and one on their opponents, the bookie
takes in $12 and pays out $11. His profit is $1
out of every $12 wagered, or 8⅓%.

And that is why, unless you know 8⅓% more
than the bookmakers and the public do about the
strength of baseball teams, you are going to lose
more than you are going to win. The built-in odds
are against you.

As if this is not bad enough, some bookies claim
as forfeited all money bet on games that are tied
or called off. You can avoid this boost in the odds
against you by making sure you are not dealing with
a fellow using this rule.

Suppose, however, that those Giants of yours are
favored to win by odds of 7 to 5. The bookie will
ask you to put up $8 in order to win $5. Anyone
betting the other team will have to put up $5 in the

hope of winning only $6. The bookie has taken in $13 and will pay out $13 if the Giants win, $11 if they lose. In the long run he's $1 ahead for each $13 wagered, or about 7.7%.

The bookie's lines

A bookmaker profiting at this level has what is called a 40¢ line, presumably because that is his approximate profit from a $5 bet when the odds are fairly close to even.

A bigger bettor can, if he is shrewd, find a 20¢- or even a 10¢-line man to deal with. A nickel line is usually a wholesaler, who deals with smaller bookies, not with you.

Each of these drops, from 40 to 20 and so on, cuts the odds in half. A bettor out of the $5 class thus may often deal with a 20¢ line and buck improved odds of around 4%. A big bettor finds the unfavorable edge only 1 to 2½%.

Professionally operated betting on football games, and on basketball and hockey, commonly uses a slightly different system, which converts every game into an even-money bet. The pricemakers will say "Cal 3 points over Stanford." You will add 3 to Stanford's final score to find out if, from the point of view of bet collecting, you have won or lost or tied.

Any sport can make money—for the bookie.

If, when you go to place a bet, you are offered 6 to 5, you will recognize this as equivalent to the baseball 40¢ line. The percentage against you is around 8. You can cut this almost in half if you can find an 11 to 10 quote instead.

Prize-fight betting is much like that done on baseball except that bookies are even more eager to demand that bigger percentage. They find that one fighter is not as reliable as a team of ballplayers.

There is one sport—a spectator sport for most of us—in which the odds play a preeminent part. That's horse racing, where a small wager is part of the spice of an afternoon at the track for even the great majority of us who have too much sense to gamble seriously.

Dr. Roy M. Dorcus, while Dean of Life Sciences at the University of California at Los Angeles, collaborated with Mrs. E. R. DaSilva, a research assistant, to find out some useful things about the odds created when horses run. Their massive observations and calculations have been embodied in a book, *Science in Betting: The Players and the Horses* (Harper & Row).

Here, in the form of an imaginary dialogue— questions put by me and "answered" by these scientists—are the most useful things they have discovered about the odds at the race track. Using these tips and conclusions on the odds can make betting more amusing, and probably less expensive if not actually profitable for anyone of a speculative bent of mind.

But to risk more than you can afford in an effort to make money on the horses remains a fool's game. Aside from the plain risks involved, you're handing the track and tax collector some 15% of the winnings plus another couple percent in odd change.

Q. What's the easiest way to pick winners at the track?
A. Just stick a pin through the eye of the horse on the cover of your race card, then bet the horses whose names are pierced by the pin. You'd be surprised how many people do this.

Q. They *win* that way?

A. Of course. By the workings of chance they're bound to. This system has picked as many as 5 consecutive winners, including the daily double.

Q. But how many losers does it pick?

A. More losers than winners, of course. Like any chance system it's bound to put you behind in the long run by the amount of the track percentage and tax.

Q. I'd rather do my picking the hard way and win some money. What'll happen if I stick to betting all the favorites?

A. You'll be doing what a huge segment of the overcautious public does. The result is that favorites as a whole are overbet—i.e., so many people bet on them that the parimutuel system makes them pay less than they really should.

Q. Let's get down to cases on this one. What's my expectation if I hang around Santa Anita and keep betting favorites?

A. We found that by the time you'd bet $2 on each of a hundred races you'd be in the hole $15.10. Same thing, within a dime either way, at Aqueduct and Hollywood Park. Risking $200 by betting the favorites in a hundred races at Belmont turned up even worse results—a $27 loss.

Q. I've heard you can do better on favorites at small summer tracks, where form is supposed to be more predictable.

A. We checked this out at Del Mar in California for a season. You'd have had the encouragement of a slightly higher percentage of wins, but the payoff was poorer. You'd still have wound up behind, this time by $16.95.

Q. Can I beat these poor payoffs by betting only the long-priced favorites—horses on which the odds are not much different from those on other nags in the race? Maybe I wouldn't win so often but there'd be real money in it when I did. Yes?

A. No. We found that long-priced favorites did worse than favorites as a whole. On a sample where the odds were 2 to 1 or more, a hundred $2 bets produced a whopping $57.50 loss.

Q. Short-priced favorites, then?
A. Better. We tested this system in a series of 79 races at Santa Anita. Betting favorites that were at even money or less gave winners 62% of the time, for a profit of $10.60. In 52 races at Belmont, though, short-priced favorites came in only 57.7% of the time for a loss of $6 for the series of $2 bets.

Q. So on the whole?
A. Breaking even when betting short-priced favorites is the typical picture nationally. When you consider that in the nature of things more money is bound to be lost than won on horses, that's not bad. It beats most systems. It beats betting blindly by a good ways.

Q. How about psychological betting? An oldtimer tells me that the thing to do is bet the favorite in the last race of the day. By that time the casual bettors who run up the odds on favorites too high have left or run out of money. And the big losers will be too busy trying to recoup in a single race—by backing long-price horses—to bet the favorite. This should make him underbet—and give me favorable odds.
A. It does seem to work that way, although the advantage is too small to give you a real profit against the track percentage.

Q. More psychology. When favorites have won two or three races in a row, you get people saying that this can't go on. Since that idea is nothing but superstitious nonsense, this should be a good time to bet the favorite.

A. True again. And you should have a relatively favorable situation when all three of these things occur at once. That is, when there is a short-priced favorite in the last race after favorites have won several times in a row.

Q. Since you didn't think so much of the pin-prick system, what about going along with the form sheet? What will happen to me if I put my nickels all through the season on the "best bet of the day" as recommended by the form sheet?

A. We tried this theory on the fifty "consensus best bets" during the season at Santa Anita. They won precisely half the time, in contrast to only 30% wins by the general favorites. But that still produces a net loss.

Q. Most racing fans believe you'll find more longshot winners at the beginning of a racing season. It's logical that form should be less predictable then, isn't it?

A. Like a lot of things in racing it may be logical but it doesn't seem to be true. One part of the season is as good as another in this respect, or so our figures say. They also disprove that the last two or three weeks of a racing season produce any unusual number of longshots.

Q. Is it smarter to back horses at certain odds than those in some other ranges?
A. Interestingly enough, we found a quirk in this respect that seems worth knowing about. Horses at about 12 to 1 odds seem to win almost as often as those at 6 to 1 and of course pay much better. So within the range of 6 to 1 to 12 to 1 it makes sense to prefer the latter. This goes for show betting as well as win. Our information on this is from the bigger tracks. Somewhere else you might want to make your own comparison.

Q. What about betting on an entry—two horses entered as a team so that if either wins I collect? I figure two horses trying to win one bet for me is a pretty good deal. Is it?
A. Not particularly. If you'd backed the entry in every one of the 72 races in a Santa Anita season that contained an entry, you'd have ended a heavy loser.

Q. I've heard recommendations for across-the-board betting—that is, backing one horse to win, to place, and to show. Also for split betting—backing the favorite to win and some fairly long shot to place or show in the same race. Do your figures show that either of these is profitable?
A. No.

Q. How about the long shots in general?
A. In general they cost you money.

Q. Which post position produces the most winners?
A. Our dope shows that however it may look on the

Two bets at the track that are nearly always
losing ones are: betting on one horse
to win, place and show; and betting on longshots.

evidence of a few races, in the long run, post position doesn't mean a thing.

Q. How does it work out to bet on the horse in
each race that shows the highest total earnings for
the year?
A. This seems to yield small profits or small losses.
Using average earnings or previous year's earnings
does no better.

Q. How about underlays? For that matter, just what *is* an underlay?

A. It's just a horse on which the closing odds like the horse better than your newspaper or racing sheet did. So when you bet an underlay you're saying to yourself, "Aha, the bettors know *something* about this horse that the handicappers didn't know, and I'm going to ride along with them."

Q. Does this pay off?

A. We tried underlays at Hollywood and Aqueduct, on favorites, using Sweep's dope in the *Daily Racing Form*. We won a little, lost a little. Next we tried limiting our bets to horses which Sweep had assigned odds of 4 to 1 or less. This gave us a profit of about $10 on $66 bet at Aqueduct, $4 on $58 at Hollywood. Betting to place we'd have done somewhat better.

Q. Would you say that high-odds underlays tend to yield excellent profits?

A. Certainly that was our experience. At large tracks overlays seem to pay better than underlays at small tracks.

Q. No doubt an overlay is the opposite of an underlay?

A. Correct. When you bet an overlay you're backing the expert's opinion against that of the betting public.

Q. Is that smart?

A. It can be, at least in our experience. At the same tracks we chose only horses that Sweep rated somewhere between 2½ to 1 and 8 to 1. We eliminated any on which the odds failed at least to double by closing time. This gave us few favorites and fewer winners. But $2 wagered on each of the 50 races at Hollywood showed a profit of $148.60 against a loss of $29.60 for a similar series of bets at Aqueduct. Place bets showed a good profit at both tracks.

Q. How does it work to go flat-out betting on horses of a stable that has a favorable record over several seasons?

A. Not badly. But you'll need several seasons of data on a stable before using this method.

Q. How about betting on the basis of a trainer's record?

A. This is well worthwhile. Four out of the five promi-nent trainers we studied gave a profit for the season when all their horses at all odds were bet on to win.

Q. Suppose I bet on every horse a certain jockey rides?

A. This can be profitable. We found that 4 out of 8 well-known jockeys showed a profit on *all* their mounts.

Q. Did you try betting on horses by their speed rating?

A. This takes care, but it appears it can produce consistent profits. We began with horses whose highest speed rating in the past-performance charts was several points higher than any other in the race. Then we bet mostly on those that had made their best times at the same track, same distance, and within the last month. We also corrected by 1 point for each 3 pounds of weight taken off or added. Finally we threw out any at odds over 15 to 1.

Q. Well, the method *sounds* scientific. Did it get consistent results?
A. On $100 wagered in 50 $2 bets at Aqueduct the profit was about $35 on win bets, $16 on place, $18 on show. Figures for Hollywood were $50, $12, and $20. Not a loss among them.

Q. It seems to me that in claiming races you're offered some pretty good inside dope that could be used to advantage. Is there anything in this?
A. In a claiming race a horse is being offered for sale at a specified price. If he actually is claimed—that is, bought at that price—you say to yourself that someone has decided he has been entered below his class and is a bargain. Since the "someone" is an owner or trainer who will have studied the horse in previous races and workouts, the presumption is that he knows what he's about.

Q. How can I use this judgment of theirs to make a profit?
A. You might try our approach. We tried the experiment on a horse in the next two races after he'd been claimed but only if he had run again within a short time. However, if he won his first race after being claimed we didn't bet on his second. Following 50 horses this way at Aqueduct we risked $192 and showed a profit of $11.45.

Q. Daily doubles and parlays appeal to many people because they pay such handsome profits. Should we be suspicious of them anyway?

A. You can judge from our check of a recent season at the Del Mar, California, track. If you'd bet on every possible combination in the first and second races, as in a daily double, you'd have wagered $9,240 altogether and shown a loss of $2,432. Putting up the same money for parlays—placing an original bet and its winnings on a subsequent race—on the same horses in the same races would have cost you $4,549—or nearly twice as much.

Q. Not good, eh?

A. It was our conclusion from this and other investigations that the daily double is one of the poorest bets at the track—and parlaying is worse.

Q. Do you have any final bit of advice?

A. It's apparent from all this that some types of bets offer a far more favorable expectation than certain others. Favorable factors to look for include: short price and big crowds if you must bet a favorite; odds in the 12 to 1 range rather than around 6 to 1; certain underlay and overlay conditions that we've described; consistent winning record of stable, trainer or jockey; favorable speed rating; horse recently claimed.

Q. The more of these factors apply to a horse the better he is, I take it?

A. Probably. That's as far as we'd care to go. Betting on horses, you understand, still remains a gamble. But who'd want it any other way?

CHAPTER VI

Dice, Roulette, and Other Games

In a direct way this chapter deals with dice, roulette, slot machines and other games and toys by which the laws of chance are used to govern the exchange of money in gambling establishments.

Indirectly, but much more importantly, we are dealing with many questions of how the odds work and how they can be calculated.

From a mathematical point of view, dice and slots and wheels are randomizing machines. Use of them differs from coin-tossing mostly in that they are a little more complex. This often makes them more interesting, and it nearly always makes them more confusing. Which, as the gambling-house people see it, may be the idea.

So a little discussion of crap-shooting should lead us to a better understanding of probability theory and the odds in daily life. Also, of course, it can make rolling dice more profitable, or less unprofitable, than you have found it before.

When you roll a single die there are 6 possibilities —the numbers from 1 to 6. Each is equally probable, for 1 chance in 6. In terms of odds we can call this 5 to 1 against any given number. Or 1 to 5 in favor of it.

When you roll two dice any of the 11 totals from 2 to 12 is possible. Therefore the probability of each is 1 in . . . oops! No. We haven't established that these are equal probabilities, so the odds we were about to quote ain't necessarily so.

The reason for this is that a 2 up on one die with a 5 on the other is a different event from a 5 up on one and a 2 on the other. They are equivalent events as far as a shooter is concerned; but still they are separate and each must be counted.

When we add up all possible results on one die with all possible on the other (1–1, 1–2, 1–3, 1–4, 1–5, 1–6, 2–1, 2–2, and so on) we arrive at a total of 36 combinations. And all are equally likely.

Since 2 can be made in only 1 way and 7 can be made in 6 ways, the odds favor throwing a 7 over throwing a 2 by 6 to 1. Same figures go for 12, since it also can be made in only 1 way, by throwing a 6 with each die.

You can make 3 (or 11) 2 ways; 4 (or 10) 3 ways; 5 (or 9) 4 ways; 6 (or 8) 5 ways.

Here's a table summing up all this.

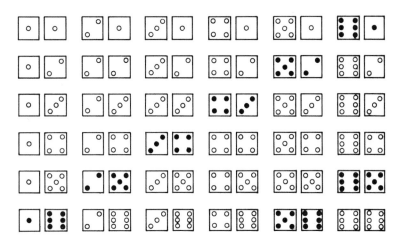

From this information you can determine (and, if you are serious about shooting craps, should memorize) the odds against "passing" on the point numbers—that is, against throwing your point before you throw a 7.

For example, since 7 can be made 6 ways and 4 only 3 ways, the odds against making 4 as a point are 6 to 3—which comes to 2 to 1. And so on for all the other points.

From such calculations you can find that the common notion that the odds are equal for shooter and fader, or opponent, are wrong and potentially expensive. For each 1,980 throws there will be—on the average, remember!—976 winning ones. Divide the smaller number by the greater and you'll find the right bettor has about a 49.3% chance of winning. That subtracted from 100 tells us that the wrong bettor's chances are 50.7%, for a favorable percentage of about 1.4.

A benevolent casino?

Whether you are shooting dice in a private game where odds offered may vary, or in a casino where they are fixed (and inevitably unfavorable to you unless you have discovered a gambling establishment with a benevolent management), you need to know the correct odds on a single roll. These "come-out" bets are quite common, and figuring is not difficult.

Go back a few paragraphs. Note that there are 2 ways out of 36 to throw a 3. So the chances are 1 in 18 and the odds are properly quoted as 17 to 1. Play poorer odds and you'll be a long-run loser.

One very interesting little thing is what happens with a bet for or against making a specified number "the hard way." The hard way means making your point by throwing a pair. Thus a 6 made the hard way is a pair of 3s; 5–1 and 2–4 are excluded.

It might seem that the odds against a hard-way 4, 6, 8, or 10 would be identical, and you might make use of the fact that the common run of crap-shooters so believe.

They are misled by the knowledge that on any given roll any one pair is a 1 in 36 chance. Each hard-way number is indeed equally likely.

But a hard-way bet loses if the number comes up in any other combination first. So a hard-way 8 is a 10-to-1 bet where a hard-way 4 is 8 to 1.

(There is 1 chance in 36 on each roll of making 8 the hard way, by throwing a pair of 4s. You lose the bet if you make an 8 by any of the other 4 arrangements, 2–6, 3–5, 5–3, 6–2, or by throwing a 7, which can be done in 6 ways. You have 1 way to win and 10 ways to lose. You can arrive at the odds against a hard-way 4 or any other number in the same way.)

The strategy dictated by all this should be apparent. In a private game, refuse odds poorer than the correct ones, which you can arrive at by applying the methods we've covered.

In a casino game, since you have no say as to the odds, accept the fact that you must lose enough in the long run to pay the casino's overhead and profits. But choose the bets that carry the smallest house percentage so that you pay as small as possible a share of that overhead.

Do this by concentrating your betting on the plays where the house takes less than 1% or a comparatively kindly 1.4%. Avoid the bets where the house percentage is higher—and it can range up to 16⅔%. This is at the *very same table* that offers some bets with an edge of less than 1%.

In a Nevada establishment, a "pass" or "come" bet will pay you at the same odds as in a private game. In the long run you will lose 1.414% of the money you gamble. When you bet the other way, you will not have a favorable percentage, as in a

If you can, find out what percentage the house takes before you decide what game to play.

private game, but your unfavorable percentage will be diminished to 1.4026, a situation created by a small rule change contrived for the purpose. This is a mighty favorable unfavorable percentage, as gambling-house grabs go.

Besides that, having made either of these relatively acceptable bets, you will be permitted to "take the odds." This means you can place a wager on the point rolled, doing so at fair odds—just about the only time such a phenomenon is permitted to occur in the gambling business. By then, wagering the maximum, you will have whittled the over-all house percentage down to as low as .5915.

Stick with bets like these and stakes you can afford—and you'll pay far more modestly than most customers for your entertainment at the craps tables. And you'll impress other knowing players and bystanders as a pretty savvy person.

If you have any doubt about the importance of shunning one-roll bets, consider what happens when you bet on a 7 turning up in one roll. This, by the way, is a fine example of the value of keeping in mind those probabilities we covered earlier. As shown then, there are 6 ways to make a 7 and 30 ways not to. Proper odds are 5 to 1 (30 to 6) against it. But the house will pay you only at 4 to 1. The difference gives the bank an edge of 16⅔%.

For a different kind of randomizing machine, one that offers more glamour and dignity and slower action, consider the roulette wheel. A ball rolls one way while the wheel spins the other, ending with the ball dropping in a completely unpredictable fashion into any of 37 or 38 numbered slots.

A preposterous opinion about roulette

This simple device is an enormously successful profitmaker for one primary reason: many people do not believe that this behavior is truly unpredictable, and they are prepared to back this preposterous opinion.

There are other contributing factors, of course. One is the pleasure that many people take in gambling, and another is the inability, often pathological, to resist playing odds in one form or another. The resemblance between such people and the members of Alcoholics Anonymous has been noted, and there is a comparable organization to help them.

If you were to construct a roulette wheel for honest, friendly play among your friends, you might include just 36 numbers, half of them red and half black.

You would then pay off at 36 to 1 any friend who guessed in advance the number at which the little ball stopped.

If the friend preferred to guess merely the color of the number, or whether it would be among the smaller half of the numbers, or whether it would be odd or even, you would pay him one dollar or one token for each one he staked—also returning his stake, of course.

In the long run you and your friends would all tend to break even, although in the short run in which we all live there might be big winners or big losers among you.

Let us suppose, however, that you are the operator of the famous casino at Monte Carlo. In order to pay your rent and your rather enormous light bill and, as a matter of fact, most of the costs of the government of your entire country—in the good old days, at least —you must take in more in stakes than you pay out.

You might add just one more compartment to the 36, but maintain your payoff at 36 to 1. You would now have an advantage over your friends—at this point, customers—of 1/37th or something over 2.7%.

Putting your money in "prison"

If this profit percentage impressed you, or your customers, as excessive, you might take a further step. You could rule that when the ball stopped in the new compartment, marked 0, all money staked on the even payoffs (red or black, odd or even, high or low half of the wheel) would go into "prison."

The player would have the option of taking back half his stake or of leaving it in prison. Should his choice win on the next turn of the wheel he would receive his stake back.

Our player still breaks even 36 times out of 37. But instead of losing his stake 1/37 of the time, he loses only half of that stake, or 1/74. Convert that fraction to percentage by dividing 100 by 74 and you will find his long-run loss to be a mere 1.35. If he insisted on taking longer gambles in hopes of winning as much as 35 to 1, he could pay for the privilege by acquiescing to the 2.7% load.

And this is precisely how those famous wheels in the glamorous halls of Monte Carlo operate to this day.

Let us suppose, however, that you are greedier than this. Or feel that if you are compelled to live in Las Vegas you should be more generously paid for doing so.

How can you double the take on most bets and quadruple it on the even chances? You can come close enough very simply by omitting the prison rule and adding not only a zero but a double zero as well without increasing the amount paid to a winner.

Instead of 1/37 your profit is now 2/38. In percentage that is about 5.26.

However greedy you are, you hesitate to go further. You feel that most players will balk at any higher price. But still, there are those not inconsiderable few of whom Barnum said there is one born every minute. You invent one new kind of play not offered in European gambling houses: the privilege of betting on the 5 numbers from 00 through 3 all at one time. Since the correct odds are not immediately obvious, especially to one who drinks while he plays, you pay off at 6 to 1. This isn't too much different from the fair odds of 6-3/5 to 1, is it?

Well, it will return the house a nice profit.

Here's the arithmetic. Player betting 5 numbers out of the 38 on the American wheel has 5 chances to win and 33 to lose. Divide 5 into 33 and you get that 6-3/5.

And when the house pays 6 dollars instead of 6-3/5 dollars for a dollar bet, it is making 3/5 of a dollar, or 60 cents, for each $6.60 wagered.

Since this is almost 4 times the margin on which the wheels at Monte Carlo have done nicely for a century, I don't think you need worry about the welfare of the American casinos.

All the other assorted bets a roulette wheel offers, by the way, pay off at the same odds as one-number wagers—2.7% for the house in Monte Carlo, 5.4 in America.

As you can see from the way we have calculated the odds, there is little essential difference between these two randomizing machines, the pair of dice and the roulette wheel.

The past doesn't forecast the future

I repeat: you cannot use a knowledge of what one of these devices has just done to predict what it is going to do. The fact that a well-balanced wheel or an accurate die or an honest coin has just produced

a remarkable series of some sort is no indication whatever of what the next turn, roll, or toss is going to
bring.

For a model often used by people working with
probability and one of its major applications, statistics, consider the urn or jar containing a mixture of

Statisticians like to use as an example an urn
containing an equal number of red beads and white beads.

red beads and white beads in precisely equal numbers. If the urn has been well shaken and you have
drawn more red beads than white beads from it,
you know that the odds on the next draw now favor
white—because there are more white beads left.
(You might be reminded of the ancient riddle, Why
do white sheep eat more than black sheep?*) If, however, you replace each bead right after drawing it,
then the situation is always the same as at the beginning, as with the dice, coin, and wheel.

There is another kind of randomizing machine of
comparably long history of which this is not always
true. It is a deck of cards.

In most card games each deal begins with a full
and shuffled deck. But there is an exception, blackjack or 21, in which each player draws cards to reach
a total of 21—without going beyond it.

It is because of this that you have heard something hard to believe—that there is a casino
game in which the odds can actually favor the
player instead of the house.

Since successive plays in blackjack ordinarily use
the same deck without replacement, the odds on
certain cards coming up in your hand are constantly
changing. If you can remember which cards have
been played and if you understand how the absence
of these cards affects the odds in play, you may fre-

* Answer: Because there are more of them. Remember?

quently find yourself in a position in which you are more likely to win than to lose. In fact, this will be true nearly half the time.

An example of such a situation is this: all the fives in the deck have been used and enough of the deck remains for the next hand. You will then have a percentage in your favor of about 3.29 if you play properly. This is pretty good in itself and it looks even better when you compare it with the *negative* expectation of blackjack players in general (about 5.9%) or of players following the most expert strategy (a loss of about half that much). Take my word for this: the calculations are too complex to show here.

What you do when this favorable situation occurs is plunge as heavily as the rules permit. The rest of the time you play minimal stakes.

Alas, there's a flaw in everything (even in the ointment, as a favorite punster of mine used to say).

The computer vs. the casino

Strategies discovered and refined through calculations made feasible only by use of a large IBM computer at Massachusetts Institute of Technology were put to use at Nevada casinos by several people, including a mathematician, Edward Thorp.

They worked. They might work for you, too, if you should wish to obtain Thorp's book or one of the others now to be had on this subject. And if you are prepared to learn to memorize cards rapidly, perhaps by use of a memory system.

The principal flaw is that the casino owners also have become aware that the method works. If you do anything to make it evident that your are memorizing the cards (casing, it's called) someone will gently escort you out of the casino.

If you want to "case" the cards in a casino,
don't let the house know that you're doing it.

Even if you case most discreetly, a clever dealer will quickly guess what you are doing from your mode of play—maximum bets, often winners, concentrated toward the end of the deck. He can then defeat you by shuffling the cards more frequently or by combining two or more decks and then splitting up this mixture into unpredictable new decks.

So it goes.

Since the other casino games vary a good deal in the odds offered, a little comparison may be worth your while. Even if you are determined to enrich casino owners, you may prefer to do so as slowly as possible.

Perhaps the best means of accomplishing this end is through study of practically any book by John Scarne: *Scarne on Cards, Scarne on Dice, Scarne's Complete Guide to Gambling* (Simon and Schuster).

For baccarat and chemin de fer, this authority has concluded, after weeks of computing, that the house actually has an advantage of 1.34% over the player and 1.19% over the banker-player.

Where any player may be banker, his natural advantage plus a bit more become part of the house take by means of a flat 5% tax on each of the banker-player's winning bets. That is, the player will be out a cent or two for each dollar he wagers; the dealer will be ahead that much; and the house will then step in and take the average amount by which he can expect to profit plus almost an equal amount more.

So baccarat and chemin de fer (sometimes known as "shimmy") offer some of the most palatable odds

Never mind the name of the game, they are all designed to make you lose your shirt.

available in commercial gambling. This does not apply to the additional bets available with these games. With these the house grabs from about 3½ to 6½%. Skip them.

About all that need be said about keno is that the odds are well against you all the way. Mathematically your best play, the 12-spot ticket, hands the house about 19%. The 1-spot comes in second at just 20%. For some of the possibilities, including the high-low groups, it's 25%.

The "big six" wheel is just about as bad. Average house percentage is around 22. If watching the big wheel slowly revolve is irresistible to you, at least take note that when you play the $1 bill you are giving away only about 11% of your wager, compared to more than twice that on the $20 bill, joker, or flag.

As to the "money wheel," a rather similar game, Scarne has found that the various versions claim somewhere between 18 and 30% of the money you put up.

Slot machines are excellent models for demonstrating probability theory. Hence the haunting tale of the algebra teacher who borrowed a confiscated machine from the police. To teach his class both theory and the folly of bucking it in practice, he concluded his lecture by dropping in a coin—and was rewarded by a tinkling jackpot flood.

What the teacher had demonstrated, of course, was a key aspect of probability theory: any possibility, however unlikely, may occur at any time. What the kids took away from the demonstration was perhaps a slightly different conclusion.

The trouble with slots is that for any given machine only its proprietor knows the odds, which may be anything he has chosen to specify in ordering the machine. Payoffs occur strictly according to the laws of chance; a jackpot is precisely as likely on the very next play after a preceding one as it is after a long, long run of taking in coins—though few players believe this.

Nourishing a slot machine

So a machine in a home or a social club may be set to pay off at even odds. One in a casino that regards it more as a lure and an ornament than as a major money-maker may demand tribute of only 6%. (It will still cost you an average of about $5 an hour to nourish one on fare as lean as dimes.)

In taverns and other odd spots, the percentage taken may be as high as 30 to 50.

Slot machines, like all random phenomena, being as unpredictable in the short run as they are predictable in the long, players have inevitably come up with some firm beliefs about them. This is part of a human tendency to search for rules to explain all aberrant behavior.

Thus there are the slot players who adhere to that doctrine of the maturity of chances. Noting that a machine set to pay off something about one-tenth of the time hasn't yielded a dime in an hour of frequent play, this hopeful person concludes that it is overdue to pay off. He lurks about until he can grab its hot handle.

A truly randomized slot machine, like the other randomizing devices we have discussed, has no remembrance of things past. The chance that it will pay off is no better, in fact, than just before the long dry run began—or last week, for that matter.

The other kind of slot player reasons that no machine is perfect, and so one may pay off better than another. He is probably correct.

However, the difference will probably be so infinitesimal that he will never in the world be able to spot it by casual observation. Life is probably too short to make series of trials of several machines long enough to determine such a difference reliably. And if he did find it, it is unlikely to be great enough to balance the unfavorable odds built into the machine.

Happily, not everything in life offers such difficulties in figuring the odds.

CHAPTER VII

The Odds in Bridge and Poker

Take 52 bits of decorated pasteboard, randomize them by shuffling and you have the basis for some of the most popular pastimes in the world. Two of these are especially complex games: poker and bridge. Both require a knowledge of the odds in a variety of situations for skillful play.

The odds that you—American man, woman, or child—are a poker player, by the way, are about 1 to 4. Or so say the best figures I can lay my hands on. Among women alone the odds, it seems, are not greatly different. This is both something of a surprise and a phenomenon of quite recent years.

Whether you play at home or in a poker club, the play will be essentially the same—but the odds in favor of your winning will not. The amounts the club takes as an hourly charge or as a percentage of each pot affect your chances of coming out ahead.

The operator of a game will often take a cut of 5% of each pot. In the course of a long evening this is likely to mount up so delightfully that the operator finds himself with more of the money you and the other players started with than is left among you.

Can you beat the operator of a game?

In this case, and assuming your skill is average for the competition you are bucking, you have no more hope of winning than you would have in a casino against any of the games that take a percentage similar to this.

With that as a reminder we can go on to the odds within the game.

The most basic information, found in the table on page 97, is how often each kind of hand will be dealt to you in your 5 cards. When the total number of possible hands (2,598,960) is divided by this frequency it will produce the next column, which is the probability of your getting that hand. All these 1-in-so-many figures are rounded off to the nearest whole number except where the decimal is too big and important to drop.

If you prefer your figures in the form of odds instead of chances, remember that when the table shows the chance of a pat flush at 1 in 509, this can be translated into odds of 508 to 1 against such a thing being dealt to you as your next hand.

You will see from the table that the value of each hand accords perfectly with its rarity except in one case, where the wild joker interferes. This might suggest that poker was the creation of a band of probability mathematicians, but I doubt it. More likely the rarity became known through observation over many, many hours in smoke-filled rooms. This imperfect method would account for the fact that at one time flushes, although they are twice as hard to get, were outranked by straights.

The odds in poker: 1

Hands in order of rank	With 52-card deck		52 cards plus joker wild	
	Ways hand may be dealt	Chance of hand is 1 in:	Ways hand may be dealt	Chance of hand is 1 in:
five of a kind	not applicable	not applicable	13	220,745
royal flush	4	649,740	24	119,570
straight flush	36	72,193	216	13,286
four of a kind	624	4,165	3,120	920
full house	3,744	694	6,552	438
flush	5,108	509	7,768	369
straight	10,200	255	20,532	140
three of a kind	54,912	47	137,280	21
two pairs	123,552	21	123,552	23
one pair	1,098,240	2.36	1,268,088	2
no pairs	1,302,540	2	1,302,540	2
total hands	2,598,960		2,869,685	

Another handy tabulation is the one on the next page, showing the odds against improving your hand in draw poker. Out of respect for the sensibilities of poker players I have refrained from including the odds against drawing successfully to a 3-card flush.

Besides, it makes a properly simple example of how such odds as these are calculated.

The odds in poker: 2   (with 52-card deck)

When you draw to:	These are the odds against making				
	any im- provement	2 pairs	3 of a kind	full house	4 of a kind
1 pair	2½ to 1	5 to 1	8 to 1	97 to 1	359 to 1
1 pair and kicker	3 to 1	5 to 1	12 to 1	119 to 1	1,080 to 1
2 pairs	11 to 1			11 to 1	
3 of a kind	8½ to 1			15½ to 1	22½ to 1
3 of a kind and a kicker	11 to 1			15 to 1	46 to 1
4-card straight open in middle or 1 end	11 to 1				
4-card straight open both ends	5 to 1				
4-card flush	4½ to 1				
straight flush open in middle or 1 end	3 to 1 (but 46 to 1 against straight flush)				
straight flush open both ends	2 to 1 (but 22½ to 1 against straight flush)				
1 pair and ace kicker	3 to 1 (but 7½ to 1 against aces up)				

You have 3 hearts and 2 other cards which you cast away. Among the other hands and remaining in the deck are a total of 47 cards you know nothing useful about—except that precisely 10 of them are hearts.

So the probability that the first card you draw will be a heart is 10/47ths. If you prove to be that lucky, then 9 hearts must remain in the other 46 cards. Multiply 10/47ths by 9/46ths and you'll get a fraction that reduces to about 1/24th. The odds against your venture are 23 to 1.

I know from experience that some people will quarrel with my logic there. In a typical game the deck from which you draw additional cards is going to be down to maybe half-size when it's your turn, with the other half of the deck in the hands of the players. Surely you can't count these; there's no chance of drawing a card that is already in someone else's hand or in the discards.

True. But then there's no chance, either, of drawing the card on the bottom of the deck or any other except those right on top. As long as the card is unknown you must count it in your calculations. And remember, we're not talking about your drawing a card someone else holds—only about the position in which certain cards now lie.

Possibly the single most important thing to know about poker odds is something quite different from what we have been discussing. It's simply this: keep your friendly games to table stakes and you'll multiply the odds against their ceasing to be friendly games.

Practical bridge

Let us now take a look at a practical approach to the game of bridge.

How can you use a grasp of the odds to make your bridge play better and more enjoyable?

Recognize first of all that if the hands you are dealt seem to hover around 10 or 11 points, that is average expectation. You cannot hope for better in the long run. And keep firmly in mind that, as we have had to note with other random-chance devices, cards have no memory. A run of poor ones does not increase by one iota your *chances* of getting good ones. (But it does give you excellent *prospects* of a change for the

better. From some runs of hands, practically the only way to go is up.)

Before applying the odds to actual hands, let's lay out some of the basic rules and strategies that arise from probability calculations. Where it makes a difference, it's rubber bridge we're talking about.

Should you be bold or cautious?

We'll begin with bidding. Here the problem can be stated simply: How bold should you be? Bid game or stop 1 short?

The arithmetic involved in this is too complex to explain here, but the results are easy to state. Let's assume you are not vulnerable and you see the chance that you will make game, or 4, in a major suit as about equal to the chance that you will fail to make 4 by 1 trick. What are the odds?

To find your expectation if you stop at a 3 bid, add the one-half probability of making 3 to the one-half probability of making 4. Three bid and made is worth 90 points for the tricks plus 50 points—the worth of a part score. Half of that sum is 70. If you make 4, you'll be credited with 120 for the tricks and will have the same part score with its estimated worth of 50. Half of that sum, 85, added to the 70 gives a value of 155.

Similar arithmetic (half a chance of making minus 50 plus half a chance of combining 120 in points with the 300 that making game is considered worth) says bidding game has a value of 185.

The odds favor the bolder bid 185 to 155. It's the better choice by about 20%. For a minor suit the margin is 25%, and for no trump about 30.

These percentages increase when you're vulnerable and go up even more when both sides are. In general you'll be wise to bid game while not vulnerable any time you have almost an even chance of making it; and when both sides have a game, go for the deciding one whenever you feel you have substantially better than 1 chance in 3.

The figures say this about small slams: Bid them anytime your chances of making them are even or better; except that with a borderline case, don't take the plunge if yours is a minor suit or your side is vulnerable.

When should you gamble on a grand-slam bid? Only when the odds in favor of your making it are at least 2 to 1.

There are many bridge hands that can be played properly only with an understanding of the odds.

One like this comes up frequently. You have a choice between finessing for the heart king and leading out your top spades in hope the suit will break 3–3.

Sometimes you can find information that will change the odds and make your decision more reliable. If you can postpone the choice for a few tricks you may then know more about the lie of the cards. Add information from competitive bidding and you may know all you need to know.

But if you are forced to jump right now while there are no clues from bidding or play, you can only say that the finesse has a 50% chance, since the king is as likely to be in one opposing hand as the other. The probability that the spades are divided 3–3 is 36%, which means just better than 1 chance in 3. The finesse is the play.

Is the queen a singleton?

There are a great many situations in bidding and in play where the odds figure. You'll find the details in books on bridge or on the probabilities in card playing. (See the Bibliography in the Appendix.) For those whose interest is limited or whose memories are not mathematical, some of the most useful information can be summarized. This is a good thing, since the calculations are often complex. For instance, when you hold 9 of a suit but the queen is among the missing 4, should you finesse for her—or try to drop her by leading ace and king? It is not enough just to compare the probabilities of 4–0, 3–1, and 2–2. You must allow for the situation in which the break is against you with a 3–1 distribution but the queen is the singleton and falls.

What to do? When your opponents hold an even number of cards, the chances are against their being divided equally between the 2 hands, since this can happen in only 1 way.

But when they hold an odd number of cards, the most equal distribution (e.g., 2–1, 3–2) can occur in 2 ways, so it is more likely. In fact, it will happen more often than not.

This reduces to a wonderfully simple rule: finesse when your opponents hold an odd number of cards, and play for the drop when they hold an even number.

CHAPTER VIII

Gambling "Systems"

Human beings over the centuries have tried in two ways to bend chance to their will—by superstition and by evolving systems.

Only in a very limited way does the latter approach work any more effectively than the former.

Incantations, tossing salt over a shoulder, invocation of a non-existent law of averages . . . none of these, needless to say, works.

Systems are more convincing, because they sound scientific, because they often are too complicated to comprehend at once, and because they actually do accomplish something.

It is quite possible to alter the nature of a gamble so that a small probability of a large loss is swapped for a large probability of a small loss. (But you can do this without a system; it's what you accomplish when you buy an insurance policy.)

Systems designed to win for you at gambling and often offered for sale at impressive prices almost invariably are based on some form of doubling. The term used for these is martingale. The device has a long and sorrowful history.

In its simplest form it is offered as an absolute guarantee against loss. What more could you ask?

You are instructed to double your bet every time you lose, and to quit as soon as you win once. The house will continue with the original bet. If your first bet is $1 and you win, you can either go home or start all over again. You're $1 ahead.

But what if you lose the first time? Then bet $2. If you win you're $1 ahead: your $2 plus the house's dollar is $3.

If you lose on your second try, double again. If this $4 bet wins, you're $1 ahead.

It sounds foolproof but . . .

Eventually you must win because tails, say, can't keep coming up forever. If you're lucky you'll start out with a string of wins, and go home well heeled. At worst you'll end up $1 ahead.

Although this sounds foolproof there's got to be a gimmick or Harrah's Club would long ago have bit the dust.

Actually there are two gimmicks.

After that long string of losers that we know is sure to appear, eventually you are going to run out of money and have to quit. If you don't run out of money you may run out of nerve when you find yourself on coin flip or wheel spin No. 11, having lost $1,023, putting up $1,024 in the hope of an ultimate $1 gain, going home with $1,025.

Bumping your head against the limit

The other flaw is that at about this stage you are going to bump your head on the house limit.

The purpose of limiting how much you are permitted to bet at one time is not just to stop doublers and other systems nuts. It is to insure the operation of the law of large numbers, which refers not to the size of a bet but to the number of separate bets. The motto is spread the risk. A limit guarantees that the house will not lose in the short run. Its percentage has already assured it of winning in the long run.

A variant of the simple martingale has been sold to crap shooters. It instructs you to play 1 chip and then, if you lose, 3 chips; if you lose again, play 7 chips—each time doubling plus 1. This method gives you a bit more profit if you win but breaks you a little sooner if you hit an unfavorable run.

Another phenomenon equally significant for a gambler or for a person planning to launch a business is the comparative-bankroll problem. This one, which long ago began to interest mathematicians, is what happens in a showdown between two persons play-

ing a fair game at even odds when one is more heavily
financed.

If you have 10 pennies and your opponent has
50 and you agree to match till one of you is
broke, which one will it be? It'll be you, by
odds of 5 to 1.

$$10 \times 5 =$$
$$5 \times 10$$

This problem has been analyzed in detail and it has been proven that the chance of winning in such a contest is exactly proportional to the size of the bankroll.

Without getting into all that, you can see why this must be so in a fair game where the odds are correct and there is no house percentage.

A fair game is defined as one in which all players' mathematical expectations are equal. If you win in the coin-tossing you gain 50 cents. Your opponent can gain only 10 cents. So his probability of winning your 10 cents has to be 5 times yours of winning his 50 cents: $10 \times 5 = 5 \times 10$.

When you go for broke

You can see why your chances are poor when you go for broke against a rich casino, which also has a percentage in its favor. And you can see as well what can happen to you, everything else being equal, in any situation you enter underfinanced against a well-heeled competitor.

This proposition has led to many an argument and misunderstanding. Consider the proposition that you must eventually lose against a gambling house because it has more money than you do. True—but you and all the other bettors together have far more money than any one gambling place or even a Reno-ful of them. So then the house must lose in the end. . . .

This argument goes aground on the rock of that house percentage, which quickly outweighs the effect of financing or a system or anything else.

Suppose you are wagering dollars on a game where the odds are 11 to 9 against you and the payoff is 2 for 1. (Don't be misled, as many have been, by the generous sound of this payoff for those odds. Two for 1 means only that when you put up $1 and win you get back your $1 plus another. Two for 1 is quite different from 2 to 1.) This is a notably unfair game but lies well within the range of games and bets offered by casinos and bookmakers.

Let us further suppose you are a millionaire and the house has only $5. Even with financing this one-sided, the house has some 50% more chance of cleaning you out than you have of breaking its bank. The house stands to win all your money 63% of the time.

Why? Because the house percentage will more often than not put it ahead of you within the first few plays and once this has happened will nearly always keep it there.

Another problem involving the size of your bank-roll is so ancient and so tricky that it baffled mathematicians and philosophers for many years. There is no house percentage to confuse this one. It is a fair game such as might be played between friends.

A justifiable risk

As we have already established, the amount you are justified in risking when making a bet or buying a lottery ticket is a sum exactly equal to your expecta-

The way things stand, the house will beat you 63% of the time.

tion. Which, in turn, is the amount you stand to win multiplied by your probability of winning it.

Thus 1 chance in 10 of winning $10 is worth precisely $1, and that is the amount you can stake on such a chance and expect to come out even in the long run. You are to suppose I am offering you a proposition based on that.

I'm going to flip a coin. If you call it wrong, you lose and the game is over.

If you call it right, I'll pay you a dollar and we'll go right on playing.

If you call the second toss right, I'll pay you $2.

On the third flip you collect $4, if you call it right, on the fourth $8, and on the fifth $16, and so on, doubling each time.

We'll keep right on going—and doubling—till you make a wrong call and thus end the game. You could be a very rich man by that time.

Now to make this a fair game we must calculate your expectation. This will fix the amount you should pay me for the privilege of playing.

Obviously you have an even chance of winning the first time. Half a chance at a dollar is worth 50 cents.

There is an even chance that I'll have to flip again and, if I do, an even chance that you'll win and collect $2. Half a chance at half a chance of winning $2 is also worth 50 cents.

There is one chance in four that the game will last for a third flip. And there's an even chance that you'll win that toss if it does. This figures to one-eighth of a chance at $4. That, too, is worth 50 cents.

In the same way, the possibility of the fourth flip is worth another 50 cents, and so on and on and on.

You need not examine the mathematics or the reasoning so far for flaws. There are none.

It is clear that your mathematical expectation is an infinite number of half-dollars. It follows, does it not, that no sum would be too much to pay for the privilege of playing this game with me?

A million dollars would be a modest price. So if I offer instead to play for the comparatively negligible sum of, say, $50 cash, is this not the bargain of the century?

Well, not of this century in any case. This problem in probability, known as the St. Petersburg Paradox, goes back nearly two hundred years to the famous mathematical family of Bernoulli and the Russian Imperial Court.

What makes the St. Petersburg Paradox so fascinating is that the logic and the math, as stated, are correct and beyond question. Yet you somehow *know* the game isn't really worth a huge sum to you.

The question is why? And how much *is* fair to pay? The answer, oddly enough, depends not on your pocketbook but on mine.

There's no point in your paying for a possibility of winning money beyond my capacity to pay off. There's a limit to the blood in this turnip —or any other.

To make the first toss a good investment for you, I must have a dollar to use for the payoff. To justify the second toss, I must have $2 more. I need another $4 to back the third toss, $8 for the fourth, and so on.

That's all very well—so far—but you know how doubles begin to mount up after a bit. By the end of 12 flips I'll be out $4,096 and I'll need an additional $4,096 to continue for one more toss.

Even if I happen to be five times a millionaire I can last out barely 22 unfavorable flips. Since each flip is worth just 50 cents to you, you should even then pay me no more than $11 to play the game.

To play the coin-tossing game of chance according to the rules of the St. Petersburg Paradox you need an opponent who has an inordinate amount of money under his mattress.

As for the $50 I asked of you. . . ! That would be justified only if I possessed the capital to survive 99 unfavorable flips and remain ready to pay off on the hundredth. The sum I'd need to have tucked under my mattress would, expressed in dollars, stagger the tongue of a bureaucrat. In pure, glittering gold it would be a mass greater than the sun.

CHAPTER IX

Genetics and Probability

Much of what children inherit from their parents in the way of physical and mental makeup can be predicted with help from the laws of chance.

Many ailments both serious and trivial are hereditary, as is a marked degree of susceptibility to a large number of others. Enough has been learned about these things in recent years to permit useful (and sometimes life-and-death) predictions about children from known characteristics of parents and other relatives. Some lend themselves to probability calculations and so may be expressed as odds.

Here in its starkest terms is a crisis that may threaten any woman of childbearing age and her husband. It is a dilemma with probability at its heart.

To this couple—which might perhaps be you—
has been born a first child with a serious congenital
defect. This may be a physical defect, an illness, a
mental deficiency.

Should you have another child?

Your decision may take an especially agonizing
form. If pregnancy has already commenced, possibly
because the nature or even the existence of the first
child's defect was not immediately known, the question may be whether to interrupt the pregnancy at
once.

The new art of genetic counseling

Decisions like these usually are far too serious and
complex to make unaided. Since they involve odds
often very difficult to calculate, the family physician
is likely to recommend that you get genetic counseling, a quite new medical art.

Genetic counseling consists essentially of applying
medical knowledge and a calculation of odds to data
obtained in some surprising ways. A genetic detective
may find himself examining tombstones, searching
out obituaries in ancient newspapers, interviewing
great-grandmothers, taking blood samples wholesale
at family reunions.

Your search for the answer to whether to have a
second child will begin with an effort to pin down
the precise nature of the defect.

There are many kinds of mental deficiency. Mild
retardation may have no specific detectable genetic

foundation. Children do vary in mental capacity, just as they do in height and weight.

Given parents of average intelligence, each child has an equal chance of being somewhat brighter than they are, or of being somewhat less intelligent. A few children of parents with average intelligence will be positively brilliant, to everyone's amazement, and a few will be noticeably subnormal. But the odds are great against their child's intelligence being as low as the moron level. Parents of a severely retarded child may develop conscious or unconscious feelings of guilt—there must be something wrong with them, they think, to have produced a retarded child. But what has happened is inevitable over a large group of births, just as surely as most long series of coin flips consist of a fairly even mix of heads and tails but a few short series of tosses are bound to be mostly heads and a few mostly tails.

How nature deals with extremes

Where combined parental intelligence is well above, or below, average, a strange leveling or equalizing effect comes in. This is something biostatisticians call regression toward the mean, and is nature's way of dealing with extremes. Bright parents tend to have children brighter than average but less bright than themselves. Happily it works both ways: the child of a dull-minded pair will more often than not be smarter than they are.

This is a mathematical matter, a way the odds work, so it applies similarly to other characteristics. Tall parents tend to have children who are tall but, on the average, less tall than themselves. A student who makes a very high grade on one test will probably do well on the next, but not so well as the first time . . . so go the odds.

Extreme mental retardation, it appears, is a different kind of thing from the mild sort that is statistically inevitable as part of a normal distribution. Many severe cases have definite causes, most of which are known.

How defects can occur

Some of these are hereditary and some are not. A congenital defect is one present at birth, whether produced by an occurrence during pregnancy or present since the very beginning, hidden within the genetic material inherited from the parents. Such a defect may be related to a gene passed on by a parent or originate from a chromosomal accident involving seemingly normal genes.

Chromosomes occur in pairs and are the vehicles of inheritance. Man has a total of 46 chromosomes, 23 pairs. Children obtain half their chromosomal makeup from each parent: that is, 23 from their mother and 23 from their father. Genes are the units of chromosomal structure which determine a child's characteristics. Each chromosome contains thousands of genes; to be conservative let us assume a human being has 5,000 genes. Thus there could be 2^{5000} different combinations of genes. The total number of electrons and protons estimated by physicists to exist in the entire universe is small by comparison.

Two genes forming a pair might be the same. When this is the case the offspring would breed "true" as to that characteristics. When two genes in a pair are not the same, the gene which expresses itself is termed dominant because it blocks the "weaker" one, which is called recessive, from expressing itself. For some traits both genes express themselves, neither one being dominant; at times one exhibits only partial dominance.

Many congenital defects are due, not to a faulty gene expressing itself, but to a chromosomal accident. Such is the case with Down's syndrome. If a child is

Hereditary characteristics as a rule are either dominant or recessive. The dominant characteristics, to put the matter too simply, express themselves, while the recessive tend not to.

severely retarded, with an IQ below 50, the odds are 1 in 5 that the afflicted child has Down's syndrome. Also known as Mongolian idiocy, Down's syndrome manifests other symptoms such as eyefolds that appear Mongoloid, heart abnormalities, short stocky body with a thin neck, and a peculiar palm print with a four-finger fold termed a simian crease.

An afflicted child's chances

The afflicted child has about 1 chance in 12 of reaching the age of forty. Mongolism occurs about once in 600 births, but far less frequently if the mother is young, when the chances are 1 in 2,000. As the mother approaches the end of her fertile years the probability of a Mongoloid birth greatly increases (1 in 50).

The chromosomal accident within the mother (termed non-disjunction) which produces Mongolism results in the child receiving an extra chromosome, yielding a total of 47 chromosomes for the afflicted child. A mother of such a child runs 3 times the normal risk of giving birth to a second child also afflicted by the syndrome. If she is young the chances are 1 in 200 that the second child will be afflicted; if she is approaching the end of her childbearing years the chances increase to 1 in 34.

There is one rare exception. Where the mother is found to have an abnormal chromosome, the chances can approach 1 in 3 that the child will be afflicted— a most considerable risk.

If a child shows a mental or physical defect at birth or in the early months of life, the odds are quite high that the abnormality is hereditary. The chances that a future child will share the misfortune can then be calculated and expressed in the form of probability.

The same probability also applies to the first born, a fact that may be of great importance to two people contemplating marriage. But here, since there are no children to estimate from, the genetic detective must rely on what can be learned about the couple: their ancestry and their relatives.

Every normal human being transmits his characteristics through 23 pairs of chromosomes. Of each pair, only one goes into each of his sperm cells (or of her ova cells). Thus there is an even chance that a child will inherit a chromosome bearing the normal or defective characteristic in question if it occurs in either parent.

A dominant characteristic will usually show itself. So if either parent has it, the chances of its appearing in their child will be 1 in 2.

Odds on recessive traits

But a recessive trait will appear only if inherited from *both* sides of the family. The fact that a first child has it is evidence that it exists in both father and mother. But just as tossing 2 coins will produce 2 heads only once in 4 tries (on the average, remember!), so is there 1 chance in 4 that both recessive genes will appear in any given child.

So you might say that a dominant trait is more powerful, since it requires only one parent to transmit it. But a recessive trait is sneakier, since it can be passed on by two parents, neither of whom shows it.

On rare occasions a dominant trait may appear in a child neither of whose parents has the characteristic. This genetic change is called a mutation, the result of something that has just occurred in the gene, possibly from exposure to X-rays or other radiation that is all around us—increasingly so as nuclear testing continues.

Genetics in history

It is believed that such a mutation arose in Queen Victoria or her mother, making Victoria a carrier of hemophilia, and that this led to many hemophiliac descendants. It can be argued that this mutation changed the course of history. Among royal descendants afflicted was the Czarevitch of Russia, whose condition led to the rise to power of Rasputin, a factor in bringing about the Russian Revolution.

Not all hereditary characteristics are simply dominant or recessive. Some, like hemophilia, are sex-linked, and some, such as baldness, are sex-limited. Others show incomplete dominance or are qualified, irregular, or multiple, and follow patterns of their own. With traits of these types the risks are generally much reduced.

In another chapter we noted that the sex of your coming child remains about a 50–50 proposition no matter how many girls you've already had. In the United States the odds against twins are now about 110 to 1, but are far lower for older mothers. Among Amish women, who often continue childbearing into later ages, and Irish, who marry late, odds may be only half so great—possibly 50 to 1.

The odds against triplets can be estimated by squaring those against twins; against quads by cubing. Quints are too rare to prove this rule on. The odds, of course, change considerably for a woman who has been taking fertility drugs.

What else do known odds tell you about what to expect when you have children?

In the case of skin color, color of eyes and hair, so many different gene locations are involved that calculating probability figures is terribly complicated. But the following usually holds true: dark or black skin, eyes and hair are dominant. Light-colored skin, blue eyes and blond hair are recessive.

But in a number of characteristics control is exercised by a single gene. Many of the dominant characteristics of a parent will manifest themselves in the child. These include prominent nose shape—big, hooked, humped; large or wide eyes; long lashes; thick lips; dimples; straight (as against receding) chins; the ability to roll the tongue into a tube; finger length.

Can "homely" people have "handsome" children? Yes, because "beauty" is not inherited, only the many little things that make it up. The little characteristics of appearance hidden in your genes may be much

better than their manifestations in you, and they may combine nicely with those your mate is carrying. As the indifferent-looking father of four pretty daughters, I can beamingly testify to this happy circumstance.

I regret to point out that the odds on handsome parents having homely children are just as good.

Some understanding of the odds on inheritance of serious conditions is worth having. Some hereditary defects are largely correctable if watched for in the first days or months of a child's life.

Diseases that are inherited

Diabetes is an example of a disease which is definitely inherited, and is subject to successful treatment. Indeed, within my own circle there are contrasting instances. A cousin of mine died pathetically in boyhood not many months before Banting and MacLeod discovered the insulin that would have saved him. But the cousin of my brother-in-law is Billy Talbert, whose diabetes, appearing only slightly later, did not prevent him from becoming one of the best tennis players in the world.

Cystic fibrosis is inherited as a recessive. The odds against a child's having it are at least 1,000 to 1. But, as with other recessives, when one child has it there is 1 chance in 4 that it will afflict any succeeding child.

Sickle-cell anemia, much publicized of late because of high prevalence among black people, is an example of a recessive disease. When inherited from just one parent, the condition is usually harmless unless the bearer is exposed to high-altitude conditions, as in parachuting. (The defect has to do with oxygen pressure in the blood.) But when doubly inherited, sickle-cell anemia becomes a disease commonly fatal. Odds of having this are about 1 in 500 for American Negroes but are far higher in many parts of Africa. For the single-gene form the chance is as high as 1 in 12.

How can an ailment that strikes down most sufferers before they reach the age of reproduction survive in mankind? Shouldn't it breed itself out of existence? Sicklemia provides a striking answer.

In the harmless one-gene form, it gives the bearer increased resistance against a form of malaria that is both fatal and widespread in precisely the parts of Africa where sicklemia is prevalent. In this environment sickle cells can be said to do more good than harm, and their bearers are likely to be blessed with a higher-than-average survival rate.

A lifesaving affliction

If more evidence is needed of this strange provision in nature, consider Cooley's anemia. It afflicts white people in an area around the Mediterranean and in Southeast Asia—and their descendants everywhere. It too affects blood cells in a way that produces resistance against a dangerous kind of malaria prevalent in precisely the regions where the anemia is found. It too is harmless when inherited from one parent, usually fatal in the rare instances when inherited from both.

So it would seem that in some parts of the world a person born with a single gene of one of these anemias might consider his disease a lifesaving one rather than life destroying, because it would increase his chances of survival.

CHAPTER X

Statistics: The Odds on What to Believe

"Make haste to use the new drugs while they are still effective."

Edward L. Trudeau, one of the great American physicians of the nineteenth century, offered this sardonic bit of tongue-in-cheek advice. Hundreds of promising new remedies have come and gone since he spoke those words, but the advice is as good today as it was then.

How is it that a treatment can look so good one day—and shortly vanish without a trace? How could those now-forgotten miracle drugs ever have been touted so highly in respectable publications?

The answer often lies in bad statistical techniques. And statistical method is essentially the application of probability to measurements and descriptions. Sometimes for good, sometimes for ill, it offers a way of looking at some highly important odds that affect all our lives.

By applying a few things we have already learned about the odds, we can become more critical readers. We will become far harder to fool about new discoveries in medicine, political and other opinion polls, trends in national and world affairs, and what is really happening to the cost of living.

Figuring the odds lies right at the heart of one of the most important statistical traps to watch out for. This has to do with that major public enemy, the insufficient sample. It has produced more than its share of unwarranted conclusions.

Take the case of a dentifrice called Dr. Cornish's Tooth Powder, which was once rushed onto the market and touted on the basis of great success in laboratory tests with its miracle ingredient, urea. It is true that the tests had been overwhelmingly successful—but they had been made on a group of precisely six persons.

Well, aren't six cases enough? If not, how many does it take to be properly convincing?

Unfortunately there is no general answer to this question or we should all be able to judge the significance of an experiment in an instant. Considering a couple of extreme cases, however, should throw a little light onto the problem.

Suppose we're dealing with an affliction which—like human hydrophobia before Pasteur—is known to be almost invariably fatal. If a new drug should save even one of a series of six patients, we would properly regard it as at least too promising to abandon. If two or three pull through we can reasonably conclude that somehow or other it works. We need not insist upon 100% results.

But what about an ailment that, untreated, normally produces only a 50% death rate? What if a new drug pulls through not three out of six patients but all of them? How sure can we be that the treatment has worked? Or, conversely, what is the likelihood that the drug is worthless and the result has come about purely by chance?

We turn back to that mathematical law that tells us that the probability of a series of successes is found by multiplying together the probability of each. Without treatment the doctor had half a chance with each patient. Multiply together those six one-half chances and we will get a product of one sixty-fourth. There was, then, one chance in sixty-four that luck would produce so good a result. We can conclude that the odds are 63 to one that the treatment really has value.

Few actual situations permit such simple arithmetic. We must usually look for a statistician's statement of significance. It may take the form of a declaration that the observed difference between an experimental group and a control one is "statistically significant at the 5% level." While interpreting this as meaning that it is 20 to 1 that the difference is a true one, we must not lose sight of the converse conclusion: there are 5 chances in 100 that what

seem like connected events are not linked by anything except pure accident.

Conditions in which a handful of cases can give
significant results are pretty rare. Even impressively
large numbers may not be enough.

A classical instance is one of the earliest of the
group tests of polio vaccine, in which 450 children
were vaccinated and 680 in the same community
were left unvaccinated as controls. What the experimenters failed to reckon with was the low para-
lytic rate of the disease.

The not-surprising result was that not one child in
either group developed a recognizable case of polio.

When more sophisticated statistical calculations
were applied—afterwards—it was found that some-

where between 7,500 and 25,000 children would have been needed in each group. Only with such large numbers could a significant indication have been obtained as to the protective value of the vaccine.

Biased samples—ones that do not accurately represent the population they purport to—are even more deceptive.

The classical method of avoiding bias is to begin with a random sample, one selected purely by chance from the population to be studied. This is not as easy as it sounds.

Suppose, wanting to sample public opinion on a current issue, you set interviewers to asking questions of people on a convenient street corner. Would you get a sample representative of the nation? Not necessarily. First of all, your city may not be representative of the nation. And people who frequent one part of a city may not include all economic, social, or racial groups in proportion to their numbers. If you interview at mid-morning you will tend to leave out most working people and include too many housewives and unemployed. To compound the problem, a middle-class interviewer is very likely to produce additional bias by avoiding roughly dressed men and, if white, black people.

A good deal of the numerical information we obtain or convey to others takes the form of averages. What makes averages a fertile source of confusion is the fact that there are three kinds of averages, both in statistical use and in ordinary speaking and writing. They are the mode, the mean, and the median. When we say average we usually refer to the second of these. But not always—and that's where the trouble arises.

When you remark that the average advertising man wears a gray suit, it is pretty clear what you mean. It is your observation that more wear gray than wear blue or black or brown. Such an average, which designates the most frequent case found in a frequency distribution, is called a mode.

If you keep household accounts for a year and then point out to your family that food bills are averaging $190 a month, you are using the second common kind of average—a mean. You obtained this, of course, by dividing the total annual expenditure by twelve.

Juggling the averages

Perhaps, for a speech you are to give, you want to indicate the average income of automobile mechanics in some specified year. For this purpose you should properly use the kind of average called median. This designates an amount such that half the mechanics earned less than this and half earned more. It reveals the income status of the group more usefully than either of the other kinds of average could.

Someone launching a partisan attack on a group and wishing to make the average income sound as large as possible might be tempted to use a mean instead. The reason: for most groups, the mean will be substantially higher than the median because of the effect of a small number of exceptionally high incomes. This leads to a remarkable effect. If the average income given for a group is a mean, most of its members will be below average.

An extreme instance is offered in a rural neighborhood I know. A snob living there once calculated that the average income of his neighbors was $25,000. But when a school bond issue came up for voter approval, he campaigned against it on the plea that taxes were already beyond the capacity of these people to pay. After all, their incomes averaged only $5,000. . . .

The latter figure is a median. It represents quite accurately the true income level of this neighborhood, 90% of which is made up of wage earners and retired people. Fifteen of the 30 families have incomes under $5,000, and the rest have more. So that provides a median of $5,000 and verifies the contention that any tax increase would be a burden.

It can be true as well as misleading

The larger figure is true, too, in its misleading way. It is the mean, the arithmetic average. It is the result

of adding in the incomes of three millionaires who have vacation homes at one end of the neighborhood. These three account for more of the total than do the incomes of all the other 27 families combined.

You may have read at one time conclusions from a widely published survey that a far greater proportion of factory workers die of tuberculosis than professional men. This proved something shocking about factory working conditions . . . or did it? No.

This is an example of what can happen when you compare the noncomparable—or the fallacy of the missing fact. There are many factory workers at the susceptible ages of 17 to 21 and, naturally, hardly any lawyers or doctors. More sophisticated researchers eventually grouped the deaths to arrive at age-adjusted mortality rates. With the groups thus made comparable, differences in death patterns turned out to be far less striking. The new figures revealed less than the old ones, but what they revealed at least had the virtue of being so.

Another splendid old example of the noncomparability fallacy was the navy's recruiting boast that it was safer to be in the navy than out of it, even in wartime. Factual basis was a death rate among the

It's easy to "prove" that it's safer to be in the navy even in wartime than in, say, New York City, as suggested by the drawing on the opposite page. The navy sample is mainly youngsters; the city sample must take in all kinds of people, including the elderly.

sailors of only 9 per thousand during the Spanish–American War, while for civilians in New York City it was 16 per thousand.

Comparing the noncomparable

The gimmick is that the navy's figures were based on young men who had passed rigorous physical examinations. The civilians included the usual proportion of old folks, infants, and rejectees. So again the groups were so far from comparable that any conclusion was unwarranted.

An understanding of odds will often permit you to estimate the value of a figure cited to you as an average. When a reliable source, such as the Bureau of the Census, tells you the average income for some type of family was $9,740 last year it will append some additional information.

It will tell you, first of all, what kind of average has been used. For reasons we've already examined, it will be a median for most income estimates.

And then it will tell you how precise you may believe the figure to be. This the Bureau does by a statement that the chances are 19 out of 20 (making odds of 19 to 1) that the average is in error by no more than, say, $72 either way.

Being told frankly that there is 1 chance in 20 that the presented figure is off by quite a few dollars is far less impressive than the more usual form—which is an unqualified statement of incredible precision. Incredible, that is, if you stop to think how few things are knowable with precision.

Is the figure too precise?

So when you meet a flat statement of this kind, consider whether it may not be kin to the published scare figure that heroin addicts steal $4,400,000,000 worth of goods in New York City each year. That's precise enough to sound as if there were real information behind it.

But a curious investigator discovered how it was obtained. Someone had taken an estimate of 100,000 addicts, multiplied this by the cost of an average habit of $30 a day, and this in turn by 365 days. This unknown statisticulator had then assumed that to raise $30 an addict must steal four times that value in merchandise, fencers being the discounters they are. Slightly rounded off, this does indeed come to upwards of $4-billion.

Aside from being iffy all the way, the figure suffers from the fact that the value of *all* the goods known to be stolen in New York in a year comes to a fraction of that amount. Soberer heads now guess that one-tenth the original figure is probably closer to the truth.

It is an instance to remember whenever you encounter a palpably unknowable figure. And you can safely guess that the more precisely the figure is stated ("87% of the people in Northern Thailand now live within a day's journey of a main road") the greater the odds it is worthless.

CHAPTER XI

Insurance: Betting Your Life

If you gamble you're reckless.

If you buy insurance you're thrifty.

These are things that "everybody knows." Yet buying insurance and gambling are amazingly similar. And when you take a look at the odds you may find that you are paying for insurance that is a poorer risk than some of the opportunities that Reno offers. And a gamble that is worse than a Reno gamble is a pretty poor thing, especially if you aren't getting any fun out of it.

When you buy insurance you usually bet small sums regularly against a slight chance of collecting a large sum.

This is just what you do when you indulge in gambling in many of its forms—playing a slot machine or the numbers on a roulette wheel or buying lottery tickets.

If you are an average buyer, or gambler, you will pay much more in the long run than you will get back.

There is one essential difference, of course. A gambling win may come at any time. It makes little difference to the gambling establishment and none at all to the slot machine or the roulette wheel whether you are flush or just about broke. But, as a matter of principle, insurance pays off when you need it most.

The subject of insurance—a vast one—is considered in depth in other volumes in this series. We need to consider it here at least briefly, however, because you can be a better buyer of insurance if you understand the odds that are involved.

When confronted by an insurance decision, begin by applying the expectation test.

Any insurance policy that can be expected— on the average and over the years—to show a cash profit for you is worth buying.

Life insurance premiums are based on average expectations of large numbers of people. If your life expectancy is below normal and you can obtain insurance without a boost in premiums, you are being offered a good gamble. You should probably take it.

If you have good health, conservative habits, and ancestors who lived to ripe ages, you're part of the great group who will put more money into life insurance than their heirs will collect. The odds say you should skip life insurance. But the risk, however small, of leaving your family poorly provided for argues strongly for buying insurance anyway. We'll look into the question of balancing odds against other aspects in a minute.

Your annual decisions about your automobile insurance call even more definitely for an assessment of the odds.

But what are the odds? How can you estimate the likelihood of having an accident? How can you guess how costly it will be? You can't. But fortunately there is another, and simpler, way to get at the expectation. Without any calculating at all.

What premiums have to cover

From the fact that at least some insurance companies are showing profits on their automobile business, with the industry as a whole hanging onto more than half the premiums collected, it is easily guessed that the normal expectation is heavily against the average driver. The premiums he pays must cover all the claims plus the overhead—which is notably high in this field, as it has to be because it includes

Automobile insurance premiums have to be golden for
the insurers because they have to cover
overhead as well as costly legal fees.

sales costs, adjusting costs, and enormous legal fees
for cases that come into court.

So if you are a competent and consistently sober
driver covering few miles each year under relatively
safe conditions, you will pay far more for insurance
than it is worth—mathematically speaking. What you
will buy will depend upon other considerations,
which we will encounter after a few more paragraphs.

Your general rule, however, is already clear: you are what an insurance man would call a "good risk" and you should buy as little coverage as you dare and as the laws in your state permit. In the long run, car insurance will tend to take several times as much out of your pocket as it will give back.

Your driving habits—and record—should guide
you in determining how much car insurance you need.

But what if you drink and drive? Or cover 30 or 40 thousand miles a year in your car? Or regularly buck heavy traffic? Or must leave your car parked in areas subject to heavy vandalism or thievery? To the extent that you can buy insurance without heavier premiums that reflect the abnormal risk, insurance is a bargain for you. Load up on it. The odds are you'll show a profit, at least as long as you can find a company that will take you at basic rates.

So there's rule one: if the expectation favors you, buy the insurance. If it doesn't, apply the *disaster* test before you decide against the policy.

This is the test that asks whether the financial loss in question would be truly disastrous, rather than merely painful, to you and your family—i.e., cost you your home, or your retirement funds, or put you on welfare, etc. You will have to judge this for yourself.

It is because of what this disaster test indicates that you almost certainly should carry motorists' liability insurance, even if it is not compulsory in your state. And even though there are terrifying numbers of drivers on the streets and highways without it. You need only ask yourself this: Could you afford to pay a death or serious-injury claim in the hundreds of thousands of dollars? Could your conscience stand

the notion of your possibly doing such an injury
and not being able to make up for even the money
side of it? The answer is bound to be: Unless you are
very wealthy you need liability insurance if you have
a car.

Should you insure your car?

Insurance on the car itself is much more questionable unless you owe money on it and the lender
insists. Of course, the value of the car is a considera-
tion, too. On top of that, if your car is damaged the
odds are very good that it will be someone else's
fault. It will be the other driver's insurance that will
pay off, not yours. (These odds are also helped if
your state has compulsory liability insurance and if
you are not in the young-driver group who contribute disproportionately to the accident rate.)

Another real factor is tax deductibility. If your car
should sustain serious damage, all but the first $100
of it is deductible as casualty damage on your federal
income tax return. That is, if a smashup reduces the
value of your car by $850 or compels you to spend
that much to repair it you may deduct $750 from
your taxable income. You do this just as you would
deduct money contributed to charity or paid in local
taxes. Of course you are allowed this deduction
only if you itemize on your return instead of taking
the option of a standard deduction. You get no deduction if insurance covers the loss and—rather un-
fairly, it seems to me—no deduction for the cost of

the insurance either. If your car is used for business, the picture changes. Now both the whole amount of the repair cost and of the insurance premium are deductible from income. So you can compare the amounts directly in deciding what insurance is worth the cost.

So buy collision and comprehensive insurance only if the expectation favors you—or if you really can't afford to pay for replacement or repair of the vehicle.

Even if you can't conveniently handle the financial consequences of total loss of your car, it is likely you could absorb $50 to $250 of the loss. If so, the disaster test says you should buy your collision and comprehensive policies in deductible form.

Covering that last $50 or so of potential loss on a car is a pretty expensive thing to do, comparatively speaking. You pay a lot for a non-deductible policy because insurance companies find the handling costs of small claims so excessive.

Note also the odds against making any great profit on the last bit of a non-deductible policy. If you pay an extra $20 for the $50 additional coverage, you stand to gain only $30 even if your accident comes within the first year. If it comes during the second, you're only $10 ahead. And if it takes more than two years to produce a claim, you're a loser compared to the fellow who bought deductible.

The same useful disaster test that discourages you from loading up excessively on some kinds of car insurance is probably going to *encourage* you to buy life insurance.

One of the most unmanageable disasters threatening the financial well-being of a typical family is the death of its principal earner. Life insurance, term or any other kind, is an answer to that problem, and so is mortgage insurance. This is just term life insurance in an amount that decreases as what you owe does. If you have a new mortgage of $20,000, that's the amount your estate will get if you die now. After 15 years or so, or whenever the mortgage is half paid off, face value of the insurance will be down correspondingly, to $10,000. On the day you knock off the last mortgage payment, the insurance policy dies too.

Once again: The odds say buy this stuff if your longevity prospects are below average. And the disaster test says buy it anyway if your family is going to need the money very badly.

Keep in mind now that what we are talking about is insurance on your life—not some of the other things that are sold under the name of life insurance.

Insurance on your life is term insurance. It should be the renewable kind, by all means. Preferably it should also be convertible (into such things as whole life or endowment insurance, without another medical examination) so you can freely exercise options if your situation and needs change.

Look to the future of your family before making decisions on insurance coverage. That is the only way to determine how much of what kind you should buy.

When you buy life insurance other than term (whole life, limited payment, endowment—explained in detail in another book in this series) you are in effect paying a fee for the compulsion to save. If you are sure that you can provide the will power yourself, you'll be money ahead if you do the saving yourself. If the odds are against that, then consider one of the more expensive policies. But don't drop the face amount below the protection your family really needs in order to do so.

Another poor strategy is paying extra for the double-indemnity feature that may be offered with life insurance—unless you're in a high-accident-risk category. If you habitually drive recklessly or interfere in domestic quarrels, then the odds do make this feature a good gamble. Otherwise skip it. It fails the disaster test, too, since if you die by accident the medical costs will probably be less than for a death by illness. And the odds are pretty fair that an accidental death will have been contributed to by someone else (or a hazard he permitted) and his liability will contribute to the value of your estate.

Figuring the odds can help you to the best strategies in respect to other kinds of insurance as well.

You have to carry insurance on your house if it is mortgaged. And even if it is not, the disaster test will probably say you should insure it. The insurance package called homeowners' is usually the best buy. Paying extra for such features as waivers of deductibles, whether on all claims or just on storm damage or glass breakage, is usually not a good gamble, however. Why pay much more for an extra $50 of coverage when the odds are strongly against your ever collecting? (Many homeowners prefer not to file claims for small losses anyway. Almost more trouble than it is worth, and can lead to your policy being canceled.)

What about flight insurance—the kind you buy at the airport for a few dollars? Here the odds are quite well known and I can assure you they are several to one against you in the calculation of expectations. Such a policy is a mathematically poor investment, though you may still want to make it on the twin grounds of potential disaster and present peace of mind.

If you have booked a charter flight to Europe or the Orient you will be urged to buy another kind of flight insurance. Charters are wonderful travel bargains but they have the disadvantage of being non-cancelable after a specified date. You pay even if you don't go.

For perhaps $10 you can buy insurance that repays you the ticket cost if a medically certifiable illness prevents you from going. For a couple buying a pair of $270 tickets, as my wife and I did, Oakland to Frankfurt and return, a couple of years ago, this impressed us as a poor buy . . . even though it sounds like good odds on the face of it: $20 to protect $540.

In the first place, if one of us got sick we'd both stay home, and the refund would be only $270. Right away that cuts the protection in half, though it doesn't really affect the odds. (In this situation two people are twice as likely as one to produce a sickness, so that justifies the double premium.)

When the insurance odds are too high

More to the point, we thought back over the years. How many days had either of us been incapacitated —barring such predictable things as voluntary surgery or dentistry—over the last three years? Not more than ten between us, we estimated, and guessed that this figure was pretty close to previous experience too. Ten days out of 1,000 is 1 in 100. We decided not to pay a premium figured at odds of 27 to 1 ($270 return for 2 premiums at $10 each) when we saw the risk as 1 in 100—that is, 99 to 1 against.

Faced by a similar question you will want to consider some other things. If you are quite elderly or in pretty questionable health you may find that the odds offered are fair enough.

Insurance like this will fail the disaster test for almost anyone. The amount is pretty minuscule compared with the tens or hundreds of thousands a life, house, or liability policy deals with. And people staying home from a European tour are likely to need money less than those who go.

The easiest way to coin a strategy is by starting at the top—the big money things—and working down.

How does all this apply to health insurance of one kind or another?

Some form of major medical coverage is the most important thing, dictated by that disaster test of ours. The first $1,000 cost of an illness can hurt dreadfully —but it is the amounts above that level that really wipe you out.

You want to avoid the experience of a man I met recently. A retired executive from a major oil company, he had about $150,000 and a decent pension. He also had a fine medical policy that came with his pension. At the time illness struck this man's wife the oil company had not thought to have such policies extend to dependents. Her illness proved terminal, and it cost just about $150,000.

The disaster test says that you should be covered for major medical expenses unless you are very wealthy, and for medium-sized ones unless you are at least prosperous.

If you are prosperous, you will want to consider the odds in deciding about coverage for these middle-sized expenses. If your family commonly runs to more than normal medical expenditures, that is a

Major medical is costly but for most people
it meets the disaster test: buy it!

factor favoring your getting this optional coverage.
So is availability to you of a group policy, which is a
bargain compared to individual ones. And, of course,
so is the willingness of an employer to split the cost
with you; here the odds become strongly in your
favor unless you and yours are almost incredibly
germ- and accident-proof.

There are some arrangements we think of as medical insurance that properly are not that. They are prepayment. When a policy covers ordinary doctor bills it is essentially substituting a regular fixed payment for a lot of little ones. These tend to come to the same thing when looked at over even so short a period as a few months. Such a policy will cost you more than it will save unless your family is large, unhealthy, accident-prone, or fond of running to doctors. You may be better off without it over the years, unless there is an employer paying a lot of the cost.

Policies that combine features of all these types call for more careful weighing of the odds.

Figuring out an insurance strategy

Thus in my family we find it worthwhile to carry an individual (hence, overpriced compared to a group plan) policy, which happens to be the best we can get. It offers pretty good disaster coverage, which is the all-important reason for our having it. It will cut medium-sized emergencies down to moderate ones by paying something like $500 out of a typical $700 hospital bill. In return for these prospects of help if and when we may need it badly, we are willing to go on laying out about $500 a year for it although it brings back only $150 or so a year by returning to us most of the cost of certain office calls that have surgical aspects.

With these examples to work from you should be able to fix a good insurance strategy of your own. Simply apply these tests.

1. Will the situation in question constitute a financial disaster for you? If so, buy the insurance.

2. If the loss will be merely annoying or painful, what is the mathematical expectation? If, over the years, you will stand to take in more than you will pay out, buy the insurance. In other words, play the odds.

3. If your best estimate of the expectation is somewhere close to even, consider convenience and peace of mind. A picture window worth $300 might be insurable at $15 a year. Considering the prevalence of hunters, golfers, little boys, and workmen with ladders, you guess it might be broken once in twenty years. The odds then say this is a fair bet either way, so what should you do?

I'd say insure it. Better $15 a year than $300 once in twenty, simply as a matter of financial shock. The insurance may also save you considerable embarrassment and pain if the person who breaks the window happens to be a neighbor or guest.

CHAPTER XII

The Rare
and the Wonderful
in Chance

Everything that happens is rare, but only a few things are wonderful.

Read in the paper that Charlie Green, of Elizabeth, N.J., has won a top lottery prize and you say, "Ho-hum." But Charlie himself is dumbstruck—as much by the rarity of such good fortune as by thoughts of what he can do with the money.

As Charlie sees it, he has beaten odds of perhaps a 1,000,000 to 1.

This is almost as amazing to the man next door as it is to Charlie, though considerably less gratifying.

To someone living in the next block it is only highly surprising, and to people living across town it is hardly surprising at all. Your point of view is that what has happened did not beat any odds at all; it was a dead cinch someone would win, probably some stranger, and that is what has happened.

What is the probability of being dealt the traditional perfect bridge hand* of 13 spades? It is 1 in 635,013,559,600.

Now consider this average sort of hand, which may even remind you very much of some you've held recently. King, 10, 9, 6, 4 of spades. Jack and 4 of hearts. Ace, 10, and 9 of diamonds. Queen, 6 and 4 of clubs.

The odds on the perfect hand

What is the probability of being dealt that hand?

All the rules of figuring the odds that run through the chapters of this book tell you that this probability is exactly the same as for the "perfect" hand: 1 in 635-odd billion.

What makes the all-one-suit hand exciting to bridge players, then, is not its rarity but its significance to bridge players. Its rarity is precisely that of any other hand specified in advance—or, for that

---

* This may be every young bridge player's ambition, but it is far from the best possible holding. Your opponents can steal the bid with 7 no trump and, if declarer is on your left, may even make the slam. So how would you like to go down in history as the player who held 13 spades and lost the hand? Better pray for any of the great many combinations of top cards that will insure a lay-down grand slam at no trump. Then nobody can take it away.

matter, of the last hand you held the last time you played.

So should you be skeptical when you read that some lucky player somewhere held a 13-card suit somewhere last night? Not too terribly. If there are 50 million bridge players in the world each holding an average of 50 hands a week (pretty generous, I think) that's more than 100 billion opportunities each year for the remarkable to occur. Since we're now allowing any of the 4 suits to qualify, this says a 13-carder should turn up every year or two on the average.

Why is it always spades?

If the reported hand is all spades, be more skeptical. It isn't that spades should be harder to get than clubs, say. But for some funny reason when you hear of such a hand it nearly always is spades.

As for the ladies in Fresno, California, who were circumstantially reported (all names given) by United Press International to have held 4 perfect one-suiters simultaneously on the night of December 18, 1964. . . . Well, UPI figured the occurrence at about 1 chance in 2.5 trillion. This is hardly yellow journalism, since the true odds come to 1 in a figure consisting of 28 digits and starting with 2 octillions. The odds are a quadrillion times greater than the reporter calculated, and there are only a few chances in a million that such a deal would occur in a billion years of practically continuous bridge play by everyone on earth.

So far most of the chance happenings we have looked into are independent. A flip of a coin is independent of the previous flips—or so we have agreed to conclude, most gamblers and many other people to the contrary notwithstanding.

A deal of cards is a little different. As you pick up a bridge hand and find—with mounting excitement or suspicion—that one after another is a spade, until you have 12 of them, what are the odds of getting the thirteenth spade as well?

In an independent situation, where each card can be any of the 52, you know the chance of a spade is 1 in 4. But with only 1 spade remaining and 40 cards unknown to you, the chance obviously is only 1 in 40. It is 10 times as difficult to get a thirteenth spade as to get a first one.

You might say that at this point you have almost used up your chances of getting a spade. Something rather like the fallacious doctrine of the maturity of chances actually does exist in this dependent situation.

An even more extreme example is mutual exclusivity.

A homely near-example is this. The most common first name among men, worldwide, is Mohammed, and the commonest family name is Wong. Isn't it remarkable how seldom you meet anyone called Mohammed Wong?

Many of the most remarkably lucky or unlucky things that happen to you will turn out to be less surprising if you look for the possibility of dependence. Coincidence will often turn out to be less than pure.

Possibly the greatest coincidence-shock of my life occurred when, boarding a smallish Dutch ship at New York in 1956, I found among my fellow-passengers the only human being on earth I was on bad terms with. One chance in a couple of billion!

When I add that it turned out that we were both planning a year-long tour, that we were purchasing the same make of automobile for the purpose, and that as it happened we met again later in the year without a trace of prearrangement you may say that I must be stretching things.

When is a marvel not a marvel?

Actually, as we fell to talking—what's enmity in the face of a marvel?—the coincidence melted a good bit. We were both middle-aged, middle-class Americans in equivalent stages of comparable careers, and the ship was one to appeal to such as us. At that time possibly only one American in a hundred was a likely passenger on the *Staatendam*, bringing the odds down to 1,000 (size of the passenger list) in a couple of million, or more like 1 in 2,000.

As for the car, it was standard operating procedure for a touring family to use a VW bus; and our later meeting, at the only VW garage within an area of a thousand square miles, was a natural product of what had gone before.

You may find you can tame the more shocking coincidences in your life by analysis like this. Try this approach also on astounding tales of the supernatural you may encounter, such as the precisely accurate dream of a death at the very hour it occurred a thousand miles away.

This phenomenon, that of the non-independent chances, makes many an occurrence look more startling than it truly is. Consider this newspaper story, which couldn't be much further wrong. It is typical of many you've read and accepted at face value—but never will again.

> Luton (England)—(UPI)—Thirteen months ago, Mrs. Pamela Claridge gave birth to twins—a boy and a girl. A few days ago, she again went to the maternity ward. This time: twin boys.
> "Our family doctor told me it was a million to one chance," said her rueful husband. "I didn't even bother to insure against having them."

To begin with, the probability that any birth chosen at random will be of twins is around 1 in 100 (it varies from time to time and place to place). So the chance that any two births—again at random—will be twins is 1 in 100 times 100, or 1 in 10,000. This is what the family doctor very roughly had in mind.

But here we are dealing with the odds against twins not twice in two births but once in one birth; the couple had had those first twins. And furthermore since twins have a tendency to "run" in families, the odds against a second such occurrence turn out to be hardly greater than 30 to 1.

Million to 1 indeed.

The odds in courts of law

Luck, chance, and the odds often appear in courts of law, where they are involved in the whole and much-argued category of evidence called circum-

stantial. A Los Angeles case of this century is possibly the prime example.

A woman was robbed by a couple. Neither she nor
the sole witness could make a positive identification
—but both were sure that one robber was a young
woman with blond hair and the other a black man
with beard and mustache. And their getaway car was
yellow.

Neighborhood inquiries turned up just such a
couple, yellow car and all.

A mathematics professor as expert witness

Courtroom kibitzers saw little chance of a conviction in the absence of any positive identification. A
young deputy district attorney thought otherwise. He
called in a mathematics professor as an expert witness. Questioned in court, the mathematics professor
gave the chances of each separate aspect of the description of the accused pair as:

... of a man having a mustache, 1 in 3;
... of a young woman being a blond, 1 in 4;
... of seeing a yellow car in Los Angeles, 1 in 10;
... of a man's having a beard, 1 in 10;
... of a white woman being with a black man, 1 in
1,000.

Then, demanded the prosecutor triumphantly,
what is the probability that you will find, at a given
time and place, a black male with a beard and mustache, driving a yellow car in which a blond woman
is riding?

The odds against there being more than one
couple fitting a precise description of a criminal
pair seemed mathematically very great—but were they really?

Multiplying these and other factors together, re-
plied the mathematical witness, the chance would be
1 in 12 million.

And that was enough to satisfy the jurors. Off the
pair went to prison.

It would hardly have been sufficient, however, to
have satisfied any careful reader of this book. And in
the end it failed equally to please the California Supreme Court.

Along with objecting that there was no evidence the individual probability factors used were even roughly accurate, the court pointed out that the factors were not entirely independent. (Beards may be more common among Negroes in interracial marriages than among blacks in general.) So the mathematical laws invoked by the prosecution were not entirely applicable.

But correcting these two flaws would have made only a minor change in the probability. The big weakness in the prosecution case lay elsewhere in the application of the odds, and to the great credit of the court the justices put their collective finger squarely on it. The convicted couple might indeed be classed as a 1-in-several-million phenomenon, but in a city containing millions of couples the odds are not greatly against finding not merely one but two or three such couples. The court concluded that there was a 41% chance that at least one other couple in the area at the time might fit the description.

Imposing though they are, these odds of millions to 1 are trifling by comparison with those that seem to say that some people truly can read minds . . . see things without using their eyes . . . control dice without touching them.

Extrasensory perception, a bundle of such disreputable practices as telepathy, clairvoyance and psychokinesis, is flying high. It has emerged from the brassy realm of vaudeville, voodoo, fortune-telling, and table-tipping to devil sober scientists.

Perhaps the most shocking thing emerging from ESP—as its familiars chummily call it—is the doubt it appears to cast on the fundamental theories of probability. Since these theories are a vital part of science —physical and social, experimental and theoretical —they're found, as we have seen, at the very heart of everything from nuclear experiments and polio vaccine to floating crap games and predicting the birth of defective children.

The most convincing evidence for the existence of telepathy and other forms of ESP lies in a number of carefully conducted experiments. Here is a typical one, done on the Duke University campus.

At an agreed-upon time, a man begins to deal cards from a thoroughly shuffled deck. He deals at the rate of one per minute, without looking at the cards.

At precisely the same time a man in another building has been writing down his guesses about those cards.

Then the experimenter and the subject get together, with witnesses present. They check lists they have made to see how many guesses were right and how many wrong.

Since a special deck containing only five kinds of cards was used in this experiment, one fifth of the guesses should have been right—in the long run.

Probability theory also says that in any test, long or short, the results will probably differ somewhat from chance. And that the longer they run the more likely it is that they will be different from the chance expectation by any given amount.

In this run of 1,850 guesses (50 a day), probability says that about 370 guesses should have been right. The subject actually was right 558 times.

Mathematical analysis of the odds tells us that so good a result would occur by accident—"lucky guessing"—only about once in 10 thousand billion billion times.

Proving things that cannot be proven

On the face of it at least this experiment seems to prove the existence of clairvoyance—seeing things

that cannot be seen. Many others demonstrate the existence of telepathy, these being cases where the experimenter sees the card or object or number in question and the subject presumably reads his mind. Equally reputable experiments "prove" psychokinesis —mental control of physical objects. In these the subject demonstrates his ability at the potentially profitable art of controlling dice as he or another person or a machine throws them.

Even more unusual are the similar results obtained in precognition. The subject names the card *before* it is dealt.

How can these things happen?

That, of course, is precisely what the scientists are stewing about.

They agree on only one thing—that among these four theories lies the explanation:

1. It's all a fraud.

2. Somebody's slipping up somewhere.

3. The phenomena actually exist.

4. The whole basis of probability theory and statistical method is cockeyed.

Scientists arguing for the first explanation quote some words of Tom Paine: ". . . is it more probable that nature should go out of her course, or that a man should tell a lie?"

The second explanation is favored by John Scarne, the expert on gambling odds and detection of cheats. No gambling house, says Scarne, would be caught dead using methods as slipshod as those used at Duke in experiments with controlling dice by psychokinesis. Any gambler who respects his dollars, says he, buys only first-quality dice, calipers them with care, then discards them after reasonable wear. Those rules, he declares, were not followed at Duke.

A great many scientists have felt themselves forced to accept the results of the ESP experiments, often reluctantly, because they cannot agree that men of good reputation are deliberately falsifying experiments. Or that methods far more meticulous than those regularly accepted in other scientific work are, for some unfathomable reason, not good enough with ESP.

These men argue that the case is proved. They are more interested in seeing where we can go from here. Is telepathy really extrasensory? Or is it an unsuspected extension of one or more of our known senses? Is ESP the possession only of the few who have succeeded in the conditions of experiment— or is it latent somewhere in all of us?

Some scientists, seeing no evidence of fraud or error, but unable to accept ESP as real, are forced to conclude that the statistical proof is wrong. The whole concept of probability must have a flaw somewhere.

Yet physics is doing nicely with probability theory, using it in the kinetic theory of gases, using it to explain such ordinary things as why a poker burns your hand if you hold the other end of it in the fire. And something called Monte Carlo method, a concept born of a roulette wheel, is used to estimate shielding needed to protect lives of atomic scientists.

Even the continued steady success of the institutions that have made Monaco and Las Vegas famous testifies to the accuracy of probability when the wheel turns enough times. Crap games depend on it, and so does medicine in assessing the value of fluoridation or a treatment for cancer.

If, in the end, ESP experiments do make a mess of the old theories of probability, new ones will be urgently needed. You have only to run through the chapters of this book to realize how many aspects of modern life hinge upon them.

CHAPTER XIII

How to Think
of Luck

Is there such a thing as being lucky?

Yes, of course there is. How else can we describe the enviable situation of a man winning $500 a month for life in a prize drawing with many millions of entries? However, if we are to believe the philosophers and mathematicians on whose work this book is based, we must use "lucky" only to *describe* what has happened. We must not assume there is a factor, luck, that lets us *predict* what is going to occur.

The man who once made 10 straight passes at a dice table in Las Vegas was lucky. (Though not as lucky as if he'd backed himself heavily and won thousands, as some others did on him, instead of about $150 altogether.) But to say, at any point, that this man *is*—not was—lucky, and to back him on the strength of his performance to date . . . that is superstition, although almost all gamblers believe otherwise. Even those too wise to give a moment's credibility to maturity of the chances are convinced that a man may have a "hot streak" and that when it shows up the odds favor you if you bet on it. My daughter, a University of California Regents' Scholar in psychology and philosophy, came to believe in the lucky hot streak while working as a blackjack dealer in Reno.

All the same, it's not so.

Alas for popular belief: there is no such thing in reality as "hot" dice.

<hr>

The long runs of red or of black recorded at Monte Carlo, the successive passes at Vegas, even the Briton who won two football pools in a season—all these fall well within the patterns predicted by the law of large numbers.

<hr>

By the time roulette wheels have made millions of spins, it is to be expected that there will have been some long runs of each color, as well as some periods of precise alternation, red–black–red–black–red and so on. And of course there will have been all those other runs not easily describable—hence less interesting—but each of them precisely as rare as any other.

To be lucky at cards, observe the principles outlined in an earlier chapter. That is, play the odds. To defeat the old saying and be lucky at love as well, let the odds work in your favor by avoiding premature commitment.

Doubling the luck in marriage

If it's too late for you, let your children know that luck in marriage revolves around these figures: 28% of men who wed before 22 divorce within 20 years; and 27% of women who wed in their teens do the same. But those who wait past these ages have only half the divorce rate of those who plunge early. It's an easy way to double the luck, or the odds, in your favor.

The odds are against a young marriage
lasting as long as one of older people.

So these figures seem to say, but in fact they need
to be taken with a trace of salt. The thing they do
demonstrate—that late marriage and long marriage
go together—does not in itself prove that the late-
ness caused the longness.

There's nothing in life more conducive to bad luck than a habit of jumping to unwarranted conclusions—whether about marriage, health, traffic conditions, or the state of the stock market. So let's stop for a sharp look at how apparent odds can be distorted by assumed causation, which is possibly the champion of all the fallacies that beset those producing or consuming statistical data.

It is dangerously easy to assume that when two things regularly occur together, one has produced the other.

One example—and it has been thrown at us regularly for decades—is the statement that a college education adds some specified amount to a person's lifetime income. The figure cited in 1972, and taken from an impressive study in a Department of Agriculture publication, was $71,000.

Does added education produce added income?

That makes college sound like a great little investment—as indeed it may be. But what is lacking is evidence that the added education produced the added income. Is it not likely that such factors as drive and intelligence and inherited wealth tend to make a youngster more likely to go to college? And that these same traits and circumstances make him

an excellent candidate for an oversize income—
whether he goes to college or not?

Stated generally, this fallacy in the logic of the odds
goes something like this:

The various relationships between A and B

Of any two such things, A may indeed have caused
B. But we must also consider whether perhaps B is
the cause of A. Or even that A sometimes is a cause
of B, but at other times is a *result* of B. And there is
also the very common situation in which neither has
caused the other but both are the product of a third
factor.

This was one of the great difficulties that faced
the committee making that famous report on smoking and health for the Surgeon General of the United
States a few years ago.

The report was full of conclusions like this: the
odds of getting lung cancer were 20 times as great
for heavy smokers as for nonsmokers. Therefore a
natural question arose. How could so many doctors
and statisticians continue to contend that this did
not *prove* that smoking caused lung cancer? In reply
it was pointed out that many things regularly happen
together without one being the cause of the other.

An instructive example is an industrial study made
some years ago. The question to be answered was
whether shortening the workday by introducing rest
periods would lower production. A group of factory
workers was chosen at random. All were then given

a 15-minute break each morning. In spite of the loss of time, production actually went up. The marveling experimenters increased the break to 30 minutes, and production went up even further. The conclusion seemed obvious: rest periods increase productivity. For a final check, rest periods were then eliminated entirely—and production jumped again.

What really was bringing about the increased production, it turned out, was neither the absence nor the presence of rest intervals. It was a third factor: worker morale. It was the knowledge that they were members of a picked group in which management was taking an interest that really stimulated them to all that additional effort.

There may be a third factor

Similarly, said these experts on probability, there may be a third factor that tends to produce smoking and lung cancer in the same individuals without either of those things being a cause of the other. One form that this might take was suggested in the smoking health report.

Since it has been shown that people who choose to smoke tend to differ in eating habits, behavior patterns, body type and so forth from those who don't, perhaps they also differ in inborn susceptibility to certain diseases.

Whatever the final verdict on tobacco and cancer, this kind of critical approach is one of the elements in being lucky. It will save you from jumping to unwarranted and costly conclusions as unsophisticated as the amusing conviction that was found to exist among the primitive peoples of the New Hebrides islands.

These people have long believed that body lice bring good health and are therefore lucky. They believed this because observation over the centuries had taught them that people in good health usually had lice while sick people often did not. It took medical investigators a while to get things straightened out. Almost everyone in the islands, it was finally discovered, had lice as a normal thing. Only when a man took a fever and became too warm for comfortable habitation did his lice (which quite possibly had brought him his feverish ailment) leave him. So here were cause and effect not only the reverse of what they seemed but also confusingly intermingled.

Luck means very many different things, possibly because it arises out of probability and the odds, which constitute a large subject indeed.

Can you use up your luck?

To many people, especially small children and gamblers, luck is something of which you have a certain limited supply. You can use it up. This is the thinking behind the false doctrine of the maturity of chances. Having won three tosses of the coin you have little chance of winning the fourth, because you have used up most of your supply of good luck. Or, having held consistently good bridge hands for an hour or so, you must now expect poor ones; you've used up an evening's supply of good luck already. You don't "deserve" any more good ones for a while.

Though easy to believe, this is of course pure nonsense. A realistic expectation at this point is poorer hands than you've been holding, true, but there is no more reason to predict worse than average ones than there is to predict a continuation of better than normal cards.

A second attitude toward luck that is precisely opposite to the first is held by the same kind of people—notably gamblers. This is the "hot streak" thesis. If in a gambling establishment you come upon a person who does not believe in this concept the odds are that you are not talking to a patron. And even most professionals, as noted earlier, find this misconception hard to shake.

Oddest of all is the fact that both these two ideas, mutually contradictory though they are, are often found side by side. It must be difficult for an ardent gambler to choose between the conviction that, having made five passes in a row, he is "hot" tonight and the opposed idea that he has now used up his luck for a while.

In a careful vocabulary "lucky" is used descriptively. The man who walks away from an airplane crash that killed most of his fellow-passengers has been lucky. So has the winner at a game of chance. So has anyone else to whom any desirable thing of notably low probability has occurred. But to go from there and conclude that this has happened because the person has a special quality—and therefore the odds favor its happening again—that is superstition.

Understanding the elements of probability theory —that is, recognizing the odds—is a safer route to good fortune. One of the things probability tells us is that there is no way to insure good luck or avoid ill, except by a total retreat from life . . . to a mountain-top refuge or a cell in an institution.

Buy insurance and you are gambling the amount of the premium. Fail to buy it and you are gambling the amount of the insurance.

So the rational response to all the inevitable risks of life is to calculate the odds and go the way they say. It may be, as we are warned in Ecclesiastes, that the race is not to the swift nor the battle to the strong; but all the same, a sportsman-gambler has pointed out, that is the way to bet.

GLOSSARY

A

above the line

In *bridge*, the spot on the scoresheet where premiums are recorded.

ace

(1) The side of a die with 1 on its face. (2) The highest-ranking card in *poker* and most other *card games*. (3) In *gin rummy*, usually the lowest.

across the board bet

In *racing*, betting on one horse to win, place, or show.

age

In all *card games*, the player who sits at the dealer's left, who is the first to receive cards in any deal.

allowance race

A *horse race* in which weight carried by each horse is determined by the condition-book rules.

ante

(1) In *poker*, a bet made before the deal or before cards are drawn. (2) Chips put into a pot before the deal. (3) To put in chips.

B

baccarat

A *card game* in which a banker plays against two or more gamblers who bet against him.

back line odds, to lay

For a crap shooter who has a bet on the Don't Pass line to lay the odds on the point number.

bank

A gambling house or the dealer in a game.

banker-player

A player in any game of chance who accepts bets from other players.

beat the board

Hold a higher *poker* hand than the exposed showing of any other player.

below the line

In *bridge*, the place on the scoresheet where the trick score is noted.

best bet

A handicapper's selection to win a *horse race*.

bet the limit

To bet the maximum permitted by the rules.

bid

In *card games* an offer to contract to win a certain number of tricks or points in a hand.

big six

A *wheel game* showing three dice in each slot with the payoff on three winning numbers.

binomial

A term in algebra indicating a sum of two terms or the difference between them.

blackjack

A *card game* in which players try to achieve a total value of 21, but not exceed that number.

blackout

In *bingo*, a setup in which a player must cover all 24 numbers on his card in order to win.

blank a suit

To discard all *cards* held in one suit; "blank suit" means the absence of all cards of one suit from a hand.

bluff

In *poker*, betting a mediocre hand in such a way as to make the opponents think it is a strong one and retire.

bogey

In *golf*, a score of one over par.

book

(1) In *bridge*, the number of tricks a side must win before it is credited for its contract; usually six tricks. (2) Person who takes *racing* and other *sports* bets.

bookmaker, bookie

A professional gambler who sets odds and accepts bets on various *sports* events.

break

(1) Luck. (2) In *bridge*, distribution of the adverse cards between the two hands of the opposing team.

bullet

In *cards,* an ace.

burn

In *card games*, discarding the top card of the pack, usually by putting it on the bottom of the pack.

bust

In *blackjack*, a total card count exceeding 21.

C

call

In *poker*, to put into the pot an amount that is the same as the last preceding bet.

case card

(1) The last card of a suit or denomination still in the deck. (2) In *card games*, the one remaining card in the deck which will improve a player's hand.

casing

In *card games*, remembering the cards that have been played and knowing which are yet to show.

-cent line

The amount a bookmaker keeps on any bet as in "a 50-cent line."

chalk player
A *race* bettor who bets only on favorites.

chemin de fer
A variation of *baccarat*. Also known as *shimmy*.

claiming race
A *race* in which each horse is for sale at a stated price.

coefficient
An algebraic term for a number or quantity multiplying another number or quantity.

coffee-housing
Attempting to deceive opponents about one's hand by speech or manner in *card games*.

cold deck
A deck of *cards* which has secretly been arranged by a cheat in a certain way in order to switch it later for the deck in play.

come-out bet
In *craps*, a bet that the next roll will produce a number or a certain combination.

conditions, book of
In *racing*, the rules governing the meet.

congenital
Existing at birth.

contract
In *bridge*, the obligation to win a certain minimum number of tricks.

conventions
In *bridge*, an agreement made in advance by partners on how to exchange information by bids and plays.

cover
(1) To accept a wager. (2) To place a bet on a gambling layout. (3) In *bingo*, to cover a drawn or called number on a card by placing a marker over it.

cowboy
In *cards*, a king.

craps
A gambling *game* with dice.

croupier
A casino employee who conducts a game, collects and pays off losing and winning bets.

cut
(1) To divide a pack of *cards* into two or more packets to put them in a different order. A "false cut" leaves the deck or part of the deck in its original position. (2) A house charge, in the form of a percentage of the money wagered.

cut-edge dice
In *craps*, *crooked* dice made so by having some edges cut at a 60° angle and others at an angle of 45°. They tend to fall towards the 60° cut.

D

daily double
In *racing*, a wager in which the bettor picks the winners of two specified races.

dead card
A card already played or one that cannot be played for any reason.

declare
In *bridge*, call, bid, or name the trump.

deuce
(1) In *craps*, a die with two spots. (2) In *cards*, a 2-spot card.

dominant trait
A physical characteristic that is more apt to be inherited than a recessive one.

don't pass line
In *craps*, the place where you bet against the dice.

double down
In *blackjack*, doubling the amount of the original wager on the first two cards and being limited to drawing only one card.

double-fault
In *tennis*, failing twice to place the ball in the service court, thereby losing a point.

doubleton
In *cards*, two cards in a suit held in a hand after the first deal.

doubling
(1) In many games, doubling the size of the previous bet. (2) In *bridge*, a method of gaining or losing extra points.

Down's syndrome
The symptoms of Mongoloid idiocy.

draw
To pull or receive cards from a deck.

duffer
In *golf,* an unskillful player.

E

even payoff
Winning as much as you bet.

exacta
In *horse racing*, a bet on both the first- and second-place finishers in the right order.

F

face card
In *cards*, a king, queen or jack.

fade
To cover part or all of the shooter's wager in *craps*.

fader
In *craps*, one who fades.

favorite
In *racing*, the horse most bettors believe will win.

field
(1) In *racing*, several horses considered as one betting entry in a race. (2) In *bank craps*, a space containing a set of numbers. These may be either 2, 3, 4, 9, 10, 11 and 12; or 2, 3, 5, 9, 10, 11 and 12.

finesse
In *bridge*, playing a card lower than one outstanding, in hopes that the high-card is in the hand of the opponent who has already played.

flat bet
In *craps*, a side bet made by players that the shooter will lose or win.

flats
In *craps*, dice which have been shaved to make them somewhat brick-shaped and crooked.

flush
In *poker*, a hand with five cards of one suit.

form player
In *racing*, a bettor who studies the record before betting.

form sheet
In *racing*, a publication giving past performances of the horses in a race.

four of a kind
In *poker*, four cards of equal rank.

freeze out
Forcing a player out.

front line odds
In *craps*, the odds on the point number.

front runner
The horse which takes the lead in a *race*.

full house
In *poker*, one pair and three-of a kind.

furlong
In *racing*, ⅛ of a mile or 220 yards.

G

genetics
The science of heredity.

gate
(1) In *racing*, a structure used to start a race. (2) In *craps*, to stop rolled dice, usually because cheating is suspected.

H

halter man
A horseman who buys a horse after a claiming race.

hard-way numbers
In *craps*, numbers made by paired dice.

handicap race
In *racing*, a race in which the weights carried by the horses are determined by the racing secretary of the track.

hit
(1) In *blackjack*, to draw another card. (2) In *numbers*, to win.

hole cards
In *stud poker*, the cards dealt to a player face-down.

hot horse
(1) In *racing*, a horse that bettors are backing strongly. (2) A horse "inside information" is backing. (3) A horse promoted to win by a professional tout.

house
The person or organization that provides housing for games of chance. It may charge a fee for its use, or a cut of the pot.

I

information horse
A "hot horse" believed to be backed by a big gambling group.

insurance bet
(1) In *craps*, two or more bets made in an attempt to insure one or the other. (2) In *blackjack*, a bet that the dealer does not hold an ace and a picture card or an ace and a 10 when he has an ace or 10 showing.

J

joker
In *poker*, an extra card furnished with each deck, occasionally used as a "wild" card, that may substitute for any other card.

K

keno
A variation of bingo.

kicker
In *draw poker*, an extra card kept with a pair or three of a kind in the hope of improving the draw.

kitty
(1) An amount set aside from the stakes of a game for expenses. (2) A pool into which special bets go and from which special bonuses can be collected.

knave
In *cards*, a jack.

L

lady
In *cards*, a queen.

lay the odds
In *craps*, betting that a point, box or place number (4, 5, 6, 8, 9, 10) will not appear before a 7 does. The bettor who bets that a point, box or place number will show before a 7 is said to be taking the odds.

lead
In *bridge*, the card first played to a trick.

let it ride
To leave the original bet plus the winnings on the table and wager the whole once more.

line bet
In *roulette*, a bet on six numbers in two rows (of three each), the rows running across the layout.

little joe
In *craps*, the point 4.

long-priced favorite
In *racing*, a horse on which the odds are close to the odds on the others in the race.

longshot
In *racing*, a horse with little chance of winning.

lottery
A gamble in which many "chances" are sold and a blind drawing is held for prizes to be distributed.

M

maiden
In *racing*, a horse which has yet to win its first race.

mare
A female horse more than five years old.

martingale
A *gambling system* in which a player doubles his bet each time he loses, quits after his first win.

master card
In *cards*, the highest card of a suit still to be played.

match
In *tennis*, a completed contest between two players or two teams of doubles.

match race
In *racing*, a race between two outstanding horses with the winner taking all.

mean
In *statistics*, an average obtained by adding a set of figures and dividing by the number of figures in the set.

median

In *statistics,* the figure which divides any given group in half for any reason; e.g., half of the workers earn more than $5,000, half less. The median is $5,000.

meld

(1) in *gin rummy,* a set of cards, either three or four of the same kind, or three or more cards of the same suit in sequence. (2) A combination of cards that counts in *pinochle.*

mode

(1) The conventional in dress, manners, etc. (2) In *statistics* the value most often encountered in a distribution based on frequency.

money wheel

A mechanical game using a wheel and a marker, with one number winning on each spin of the wheel.

morning line

In *racing,* the odds set by morning newspapers on horses running in that day's races.

miss a pass

In *craps,* failing to make a point.

mudder

A horse able to run well on a muddy track.

N

natural

(1) in *blackjack,* a high combination of two cards, a 10-spot and an ace, for example. (2) In *poker,* a ranking hand without a wild card. (3) In *craps,* a first roll of 7 or 11 that wins.

numbers runner

In *numbers,* the intermediary who picks up bets and delivers them to headquarters.

O

odds-on favorite

In *racing,* a horse so heavily backed that the odds quoted are less than even money.

off numbers

In *craps,* the numbers 4, 5, 6, 8, 9 and 10 except the one of these that is the point number the shooter is trying for.

one-armed bandit

A slot machine.

one-eyed

Face cards on which the picture is shown in profile, with only one eye visible. In a standard deck, there are three: the jacks of spades and hearts and the king of diamonds.

open

In *poker,* to make the first bet in the first betting interval.

open-end straight

In *poker,* four cards in sequence which will make a straight if the contiguous card at either end is drawn.

overlay

In *racing,* to make a bet at odds closer to even than the morning line indicated.

overtrick

In *bridge,* any trick won by the declarer above the amount declared in his contract.

P

paint

(1) In *cards,* a picture card. (2) In *blackjack,* a king, queen, jack or 10.

pair

In *cards,* two cards of equal rank.

par

In *golf,* the number of strokes set as a standard for a hole or the full course.

pari-mutuel

In *racing,* a means of gambling, automatically controlled, in which winners are paid according to the size of the pool bet and the number of winners.

parlay

In *racing,* to bet an original bet and its winnings on a subsequent race.

part score

In *bridge,* a score of tricks but not enough to make a game (nine tricks in no-trump, ten in a major suit, eleven in a minor).

pass

(1) In *craps,* a win for a crapshooter obtained by throwing a 7 or 11 on the first roll, or repeating his point before throwing a 7. (2) In *poker,* a declaration by a player that he does not wish to bet at that time.

pass bet

In *craps,* a bet on a successful roll of dice.

pat hand

In *draw poker,* a hand which a player holds, declining to draw new cards.

payoff odds

The odds at which a bet is paid off. In professional gambling, these are usually less than the correct odds.

photo finish

In *racing,* a finish so close that only an official photograph of the finish line determines the winners.

place

In *racing,* to come in second.

plater

In *racing,* a ne'er-do-well horse.

point number

In *craps,* the number the crapshooter gets on his first roll if it is 4 5, 6, 8, 9 or 10.

pool

The total amount wagered on a game or, in a race, the amount for win, place, and show.

post position

In *racing,* position assigned to a horse in the starting gate.

pot

In *poker,* the money at stake in a game.

price line

A bookie's odds on a sports event.

proposition hustler

A gambler who offers betting propositions which appear, at first glance, fair, or even favoring his opponent. They in fact give the hustler a big advantage.

Q

quinella
In *racing*, a form of betting requiring players to pick the first two horses in the same race, but not necessarily in order.

R

randomizing machine
A gambling machine that yields random results or combinations of numbers, symbols, etc.

recessive trait
In *genetics*, a characteristic passed on congenitally, but subordinate to the dominant.

ringer
(1) In *racing*, a horse running falsely under another horse's name. (2) In *horseshoes*, a toss in which a shoe encircles the stake and earns the most points.

round robin
In *racing* and *sports*, a bet placed off-track with a bookie in which all possible two or three parlays are played on three or more horses or teams.

royal flush
In *poker*, a solid sequence of cards of one suit topped by an ace.

rubber
In *bridge*, winning two out of three games is to make rubber.

S

sandbag
In *cards*, to check with a strong hand, with the hope that another player will bet and the bet can then be raised.

scalpers
In *sports*, bettors who make bets on two opposing teams with different bookmakers in such a way that they gain an advantage in the odds.

serve
In *tennis*, to drive the ball into the opponent's service court.

set
(1) In *tennis*, the unit by which matches are determined. (2) In *bridge*, to cause the opposing team to fail to fulfill their contract.

shooter
In *craps*, the player rolling the dice.

short-priced favorite
In *racing*, a horse favored to win at even odds or less.

show
In *racing*, to come in third.

silks
In *racing*, the uniform of a jockey, displaying the stable's colors.

singleton
In *cards*, one card of a suit in a hand.

slam, grand and small
In *bridge*, taking all 13 tricks is a grand slam; 12 make a small.

sluff
In *cards*, a discard.

snake-eyes
In *craps*, two 1-spots.

speed rating
In *racing*, the rating given to a horse based on many factors: his last win, weight carried, track condition, etc.

split-betting
In *racing*, placing a bet on the favorite to win while at the same time backing a longshot in the same race.

spot
In *sports*, to give a beneficial handicap to a person or team.

stand-off
(1) In *blackjack*, a tie or cancellation. (2) In *craps*, an arrangement to keep a wrong bettor from winning if the shooter does not make a point on his first roll.

steeplechase
In *racing*, a course of two to four miles with ten to twenty hurdles or jumps.

straight
In *poker*, a hand containing five cards in sequence, but in two or more suits.

straight flush
In *poker*, a hand containing five sequential cards, all in the same suit.

system
A method of betting (usually based on mathematics) regularly used by a player.

T

three of a kind
In *poker*, three cards of equal rank.

tote board
In *racing*, the board which shows the total bets and the approximate odds on the horses while the betting windows are open. After the race is run, the board displays the payoff prices on the first three horses, and designates the horse that came in fourth.

tricks
In *bridge*, units of measurement of points won.

U

underlay
In racing to bet at greater odds than indicated by the morning line.

undertricks
In *bridge*, the number of units by which the declarer fails to make his contract.

V

vulnerable
In *bridge*, a team that has completed a game towards rubber is said to be vulnerable. This means that subsequent premiums and penalties will be higher for that team in that rubber.

void
In *cards*, a suit not represented in a hand.

W

widow
In *cards*, the last unplayed card of a suit.

wild card
A card whose holder may claim that it represents any rank of any suit.

wrong bettor
In *craps*, a player who bets against the dice.

BIBLIOGRAPHY ON GAMES OF CHANCE

Space excludes an explanation of the rules of the various games mentioned or discussed in this book. Here is a brief listing of authoritative sources on the subject.

Games of Chance

Cardano, Gerolamo: *The Book on Games of Chance*. Holt, Rinehart and Winston, 1961.

Goren, Charles H.: *Go with the Odds*. The Macmillan Company, 1969.

Jacoby, Oswald: *Oswald Jacoby on Gambling*. Hart Publishing Company, Inc., 1963.

Mirs, Julio A.: *Mathematical Teasers*. Barnes & Noble, Inc., 1970.

Morehead, Albert H.: *The Complete Guide to Winning Poker*. Simon and Schuster, 1967.

Scarne, John: *Scarne's Complete Guide to Gambling*. Simon and Schuster, 1961.

Wilson, Allan N.: *The Casino Gambler's Guide*. Harper & Row, Publishers, 1970.

Wykes, Alan: *The Complete Illustrated Guide to Gambling*. Doubleday & Company, Inc., 1964.

INDEX

A

Above the line, defined, 183
Ace, defined, 183
Across the board betting, 183
Additive rule of probability, 10, 14
Age, defined, 183
Algebra, use in figuring odds, 30–35
Allowance race, defined, 183
Americans as bettors, 51
Anemia
  Cooley's, 127
  sickle-cell, 126–127
Ante, defined, 183
Aqueduct race track, 64, 69, 70, 71
Arithmetic average, 136–137
Assumed causation in statistical data, 177–180
Automobile insurance, 142–144
  collision, 147
  disaster test and, 145, 148
  non-deductible policies, 146–147
  tax deductibility and, 146–147
Averages
  arithmetic, 136–137
  mean, 135, 185
  median, 135, 185
  mode, 134, 186

B

Babies
  birth defects in, 116, 120–121, 123
  predicting intelligence of, 117–118
  predicting multiple births, 124
  predicting sex of, 16–24, 34–35, 123–124
Baccarat, 88–90
Bank, defined, 183
Banker-player, defined, 183
Bankrolling a bet, 107–109
  house percentage effects on, 109–111
  opponent's bankroll and, 113–114
Banting and MacLeod, 126
Baseball games, bookmaker's odds on, 59–60
Basketball games, bookmaker's odds on, 60
Beat the board, defined, 183
Belmont race track, 64, 65
Bernoulli family, 112
Best bet, defined, 183
Betting: The Players and the Horses (Dorcus and DaSilva), 62
Biased samples, 133–137
  interviewers and, 134
  statistical average in, 135–139
Bid, defined, 183
Big six game, 90, 183
Bingo, 40, 48–49
Binomial, defined, 183
Birth defects, odds on, 116, 120–121, 123, 124
Blackjack, 85–86
Blackout, defined, 183
Blank a suit, defined, 183
Bluff, defined, 183
Book, defined, 183
Bookmaker
  -cent line, 183
  defined, 183
  profit lines, 60–61
  sports events odds, 59–60
Break, defined, 183
Bridge, 99–104
  above the line in, 183
  bidding in, 101–103
  finessing in, 102–104, 184
  grand slams, 102, 187
  perfect hands in, 158–159, 160
  point expectations, 100

singleton, 187
small slams, 102, 187
Bullet, defined, 183
Bureau of the Census, 138
Burn, defined, 183
Bust, defined, 183

C

California Supreme Court, 165
Call, defined, 183
Card games, 84–89
  age in, 183
  baccarat, 88–90, 183
  blackjack, 85–86
  casing in, 87, 183
  chemin de fer, 88–90, 184
  figuring odds in, 85–86, 96, 97, 98
  memory system used in, 86–88
  operator's cut, 95
  singleton, 187
  wild card, defined, 187
  see also Bridge; Glossary; Poker
Casing, defined, 183
Casino gambling, 9, 22, 26–27, 49
  in America, 82–83
  house percentage in, 76–77
  in Monte Carlo, 81–82, 83
  systems for, 105–111
  see also specific games
Causation theory
  assumed causation, 177–180
  third factor and, 178
-Cent line, 60, 183
Chemin de fer, 88–90, 184
Children, see Babies
Chromosomal accident, 119, 120–121
Chromosomes, see Inheritance
Claiming races, 71
Clairvoyance, 166, 168
Coeffecient, 184

189

Coffee-housing, defined, 184
Coincidence, dependent factors in, 161–162
Coin flips
   gambling systems for, 112–113
   law of large numbers and, 35–37
   probability and, 22, 26–28
   self-calculating triangle and, 34–35
   see also Maturity of chances doctrine
Coin matching, 108–109
Cold deck, defined, 184
Come-out bet, defined, 184
Congenital defects, 117, 119
Contract, defined, 184
Cooley's anemia, 127
Courts of law, odds in, 163–166
Cover, defined, 184
Cowboy, defined, 184
Craps, 74-79, 84, 107
   flat bet in, 184
   hard-way numbers, 185
   see also Dice; Glossary
Croupier, defined, 184
Cut, defined, 184
Cystic Fibrosis, 126
Czarevitch of Russia, 123

D

Daily doubles, 72, 184
Daily Racing Form, 69
DaSilva, E. R., interview with, 62–72
Del Mar, California race track, 64, 72
Department of Agriculture, 177
Deuce, defined, 184
Diabetes, 126
Dice, 74–79, 84
   come-out bet in, 184
   cut-edge, 184
   doubling systems used in, 107

house percentage and, 76–79
   one-roll bets on, 79
   rolling odds on, 74
   see also Craps; Glossary
Diseases, odds on inheriting, 126–127
Dorcus, Roy M., interview with, 62–72
Double-fault, defined, 56, 184
Doubling bets, 106–109
Downs syndrome, 120–121
Drawings, prize, 43
Dr. Cornish's Tooth Powder, 130
Duke University, ESP tests at, 167–168, 171

E

Endowment life insurance, 149, 150
Exacta, 184
Extrasensory perception, 166–172
   tests of 167–168, 171
   theories concerning, 169–172
Extremes in nature, equalizing effect on, 118–119

F

Field, defined, 184
Flight insurance
   on life, 151
   for ticket refunds, 151–152
Football games, bookmaker's odds on, 60
Football pools, 40–43

G

Gambling
   payoff odds, 186
   price line, 186
   proposition hustler in, 186
   randomizing machine, 187
   system, 187
   see also names of specific games and sports

Gaming equipment and maturity doctrine, 22, 26–27, 36, 38
Genetic counseling, 117–123
Glossary, 183–187
Golf, 52–54
Great Britain, 40
Guild, Leo, 38

H

Harlem, 46
Harrah's Club, 106
Health insurance, 153–155
Hemophilia, 123
Heretelendy, Paul, 55
Heroin addiction, faulty statistics on, 139
Hockey games, bookmaker's odds on, 60
Hollywood race track, 64, 69, 70, 71
Horse racing, 61–72
   across-the-board betting, 67, 68
   betting on entries, 67
   betting on favorites, 64–65
   betting on jockeys, 70
   betting on long-shots, 66, 67, 68
   betting on speed records, 70–71
   betting on stables, 70
   betting on trainers, 70
   betting on yearly earnings, 68
   claiming races, 71
   daily doubles, 72, 184
   exacta, 184
   form sheet betting in, 66
   long-priced favorite, 64–65, 185
   match race, defined, 185
   morning line, 186
   overlays, 69–70
   parlays, 72
   pari-mutuel system, 64, 186
   pool, defined, 186
   post position factor, 68

psychological betting in, 65–66
quinella, defined, 187
short-priced favorite, 65, 187
speed rating, 70–71, 187
split-betting, 67, 187
track and tax percentage in, 62
tote board, 187
underlay, 69, 187
winning bets in, 69, 70–71, 72
Horseshoe pitching, odds on, 58–59
Hot horse, defined, 185
Hot streak, 174, 181
House, defined, 185
House insurance, 151
House percentage
  gambling systems and, 109–111
  house limit and, 107
  on slot machines, 91
Hydrophobia in humans, 130

I

Information horse, 185
Inheritance, 117–123
  of beauty, 124–125
  chromosomes and, 119–120, 122
  of diseases, 116, 120–121, 123, 126–127
  dominant traits, 122–123
  of intelligence, 117–118
  mental retardation and, 120–124
  recessive traits, 122–123
  single gene characteristics, 124, 126–127
Insufficient sample, the, 20–21, 130–133
Insurance
  expectation test, 141, 145
  disaster test and, 145, 148
  strategy for buying, 155–156

Insurance bet, defined, 185
Intelligence, inheritance of, 117–118
Irish Sweepstakes, 40, 49

K

Keno, 90, 185
Kitty, defined, 185

L

Las Vegas, Nevada, 9, 175
  card games in, 86
  roulette games in, 82–83
Law of large numbers, 27–39, 109–111, 175
Leacock, Stephen, 52–53
Life insurance, 141–142, 148–150
  disaster test and, 145, 148
  double-indemnity feature of, 150
Los Angeles, California, 164–165
Lotteries, 40
  gambling odds in, 49, 50
  government investigation of, 43–44

M

Major medical insurance, 153–154
Malaria, inherited immunization to, 127
Marriage, halving the divorce rate in, 175–176
Martingale, defined, 106, 185
Massachusetts Institute of Technology, 86
Match race, defined, 185
Maturity of chances doctrine
  fallacious examples of, 160
  in figuring odds, 21–22, 39
  gaming equipment and, 22, 26–27, 36, 38, 83–84
  and the law of large numbers, 35
Mean, defined, 135, 185

Median, defined, 135, 185
Mental retardation, odds on, 120–121
Mode, defined, 134, 186
Money wheel, defined, 90, 186
Mongolian idiocy, 121
Monte Carlo, 9, 21, 81–82, 83, 175
Monte Carlo method, 172
Mother's age and birth defects, 121, 124
Multiple births, odds on, 124, 163
Multiplicative rule of probability, 11–14
  insufficient sample and, 131
  tennis and, 57
Mutual exclusivity and probability, 160
Mutations, 123

N

Natural in gambling, defined, 186
Negroes and sickle-cell anemia, 126–127
Nevada. *see* Casino gambling; Las Vegas; Reno
New York City, 138, 139
New York Clearing House, 46
Noncomparability fallacy, 137–138
Nuclear testing, 123
Numbers game, 40, 46–48
  cut numbers in, 46–47
  expected winnings in, 48
  runner, 48

O

Odds, history of figuring, 14
Overlay, defined, 186

P

Parimutuel system, 64
  defined, 186
Parlay, defined, 186

Pascal, Blaise, 14
  self-calculating triangle of, 32–35
Payoff odds, 186
Poker, 94–99
  draw, 97–98
  operator's cut, 95
  ranking hands, 97
  tables of probability, 96, 97, 98
Policy game. See Numbers game
Polio vaccine group tests, 132–133
Precision fallacy in statistics, 139
Precognition, 169
Prize-fight betting, 61
Probability theory
  additive rule in, 10, 14
  in genetics, 116–127
  law of large numbers, 27–39
  multiplicative rule, 11, 131
Psychokinesis, 167, 169, 171

Q

Quinella, defined, 187

R

Raffles, 40
Random sample, defined, 133
Reno, Nevada, 9, 49
Roulette, 21, 31, 36, 80–84
  in American casinos, 82–83
  defined, 80
  in Monte Carlo casinos, 81–82, 83

prison rule in, 81–82
Russian Imperial Court, 113

S

Santa Anita race track, 64, 65, 66, 67
Scalpers, defined, 187
Scarne, John, 88
  on ESP tests, 171
  Scarne on Cards, 88
  Scarne on Dice, 88
  Scarne's Complete Guide to Gambling, 88
Self-calculating triangle, 32–35
Sex-linked hereditary characteristics, 123
Sex prediction in babies, 16–24
  algebra used in, 30–31
  patterns for, 23–24
  self-calculating triangle and, 34–35
Sickle-cell anemia, 126–127
Simian crease, 121
Slot machines, 50, 90–93
Smoking, 178
Spend Yourself Rich (Williamson), 36, 38
Sports events. See Bookmakers; names of specific sports
Southeast Asia, Cooley's anemia in, 127
St. Petersburg Paradox, 113–115
Surgeon General of the United States, 178

T

Take the odds, defined, 79
Talbert, Billy, 126
Telepathy, 166
  tests of, 167–168
Tennis, 54–58
  multiplicative rule and, 57
  serving in, 55–58
  winning probabilities in, 55
Term life insurance, 148–150
Third factors and causation theory, 179–180
Thorp, Edward, 86
Triangle, self-calculating, 32–35
Trudeau, Edward L., 128

U

United Press International, 159
United States Navy recruiting practices, 137–138

V

Victoria, Queen of England, 123

W

Ward, Artemus, 25
Weather prediction, 13
What are the Odds? (Guild), 38
Whole life insurance, 149, 150
Williamson, Ellen, 36, 38

ACKNOWLEDGMENTS

The editors wish to acknowledge the help of Mrs. Lorraine Prichard of the University of California at San Diego and of Joe Trotter of San Diego State College on the chapter on Genetics and Probability.

The typographic design of this book follows the plan devised by Earle G. Kersh.